LORI PECKHAM, editor

PATHFINDER • JUNIOR BOOK CLUB

Guide's Greatest Change of Heart Stories

REVIEW AND HERALD® PUBLISHING ASSOCIATION
Since 1861 | www.reviewandherald.com

Published by Review and Herald® Publishing Association, Hagerstown, MD 21741-1119

Review and Herald® titles may be purchased in bulk for educational, business, fund-raising, or sales promotional use. For information, please e-mail SpecialMarkets@reviewandherald.com.

The Review and Herald® Publishing Association publishes biblically based materials for spiritual, physical, and mental growth and Christian discipleship.

This book was
Edited by Lori Peckham
Designed by Emily Ford / Review and Herald® Design Center
Cover art by Marcus Mashburn
Typeset: Goudy 12/16

PRINTED IN U.S.A.

16 15 14 13 12 5 4 3 2 1

Library of Congress Cataloging-in-Publication Data
Guide's greatest change of heart stories / Lori Peckham, editor.
p. cm.
1. Change (Psychology) 2. Change (Psychology)—Religious aspects—Christianity.
I. Peckham, Lori.
BF637.C4G85 2013
242—dc23
2012032771

ISBN 978-0-8280-2697-0

Contents

Dedicated to . . .

My mother, Ellen Bohmer Tripp, because she speaks and understands the language of the heart.

Special Thanks to . . .

My husband, Kim, and my son, Reef, who have my heart.

Randy Fishell, *Guide* editor, who changes the hearts of kids of all ages through the pages of *Guide* magazine every week.

Tonya Ball, desktop technician, whose quick and efficient preparation of this manuscript amazes and heartens me every year.

Jesus, who died for us so that our hearts can go on beating into eternity with His.

"If anyone belongs to Christ, there is a new creation. The old things have gone; everything is made new!" (2 Corinthians 5:17, NCV).

Also by Lori Peckham:

Guide's Greatest Animal Stories
Guide's Greatest Grace Stories
Guide's Greatest Hero Stories
Guide's Greatest Mission Stories
Guide's Greatest Mystery Stories
Guide's Greatest Narrow Escape Stories
Guide's Greatest Rescue Stories
Insight Presents More Unforgettable Stories
Jesus in My Shoes

To order, call **1-800-765-6955.**
Visit us at **www.reviewandherald.com** for information on other Review and Herald® Products.

A special thanks to the authors we were unable to locate. If anyone can provide knowledge of their current mailing address, please relay this information to Lori Peckham, in care of the Review and Herald® Publishing Association.

1

No Time to Ask "Why?"

by Ellen E. Morrison

Jack Lawrence was forever asking "Why?" when his parents told him to do something.

For instance, one day he was playing with his ball and bat on the front lawn near the sidewalk, and Mother told him it would be better to play in the backyard.

"Why?" Jack asked immediately.

His mother paused in her housework to explain that there was too much danger of the ball's flying into the street and hurting someone, or hitting a passing automobile. Then Jack realized the wisdom of her advice and went around the house to play.

Another time Jack wanted to ride on the back bumper of the car while his father drove to the grocery store on the corner. Of course, Father replied, "No, son, it's dangerous."

"Why?" Jack demanded, though one would think he should have had enough sense to understand a thing so obvious, even before Mr. Lawrence explained to him that he might fall off and be hit by another car.

After this "Why?" had been answered, Jack climbed into the front seat beside his father. As Mr. Lawrence started the engine he glanced at his son and said, "Jack, you shouldn't always stop to ask 'Why?' when you're told to do something."

At once the word "Why?" rose to Jack's lips, but he caught himself in time. Instead, he paused a moment, then said, "I don't understand what you mean, Dad."

"Well," his father explained patiently, "Mother and I always have a reason for the things we ask you to do, or the advice we give to you. You should obey at once, without questioning us. Then if you want to have an explanation, ask us about it later."

They had reached the grocery store by this time, and Mr. Lawrence parked the car. Before opening the door to get out, he reached across to pat his son's shoulder and added, "Sometime there may not be time to ask 'Why?' "

Jack thought awhile about what his father had said, and he really tried to do better. But after a few days he forgot again and was back at his old habit of "Why?" "Why?" "Why?"

About three weeks later Jack and his parents went for an outing to one of the state parks on Puget Sound at Deception Pass. Picnic grounds perched near the beach, and interesting trails wound through the trees to a bluff that overlooked the turbulent waters of the pass.

Before eating, Jack wanted to explore one of the trails to the top of the bluff. Father decided to go with him, while Mother chose to stay behind and get lunch ready. Jack ran ahead of his father most of the time and was quite a few yards in front of him when he noticed that the trail curved at one spot to within a foot of the edge of the bluff. Jack stepped off the trail for a better look.

"Watch out, Jack," his father warned. "Don't step too close to the edge."

"Why?" Jack asked in the same old way. When Father didn't answer as quickly as he thought he should, Jack leaned over a little farther to get a better look at the water. Right then he lost his balance!

Screaming with fear, he hurtled over the edge. The raging waters of the pass boiled angrily below. One terrifying thought pierced his brain: *I'll never get out of there alive*.

He was turning now, rolling over in a half somersault, when with a sudden jerk his fall got stopped. He was suspended in midair only a short distance from the top of the bluff. Something was holding him by the back of his jacket. But he was dangling, helplessly, both hands and feet useless. He was afraid to struggle for fear of breaking loose and falling the rest of the way to the water.

Turning his head carefully, he saw that a jagged root, jutting out from the steep side of the bluff, had caught his clothing. The root was bending dangerously, and Jack realized that it might give way at any moment!

Then he heard his father's voice above him. "Just a moment, son! I'll have you up from there. Stay still!"

He didn't need to call this last bit of warning, for Jack was too scared to move. The surging water below drowned out other sounds, and Jack couldn't guess what his father was doing. He hoped he was hurrying, for he was growing more and more uncomfortable. Then he heard his father's voice again, close above him.

"Listen carefully, Jack," Father was saying. "I'm lying down on the bluff directly above you. I'm going to hold tightly to one end of my belt and lower the other end to where you can reach it. Do you think you can hold on to it long enough for me to pull you up?"

"I can try," Jack answered, trying to sound brave.

"Fine!" Mr. Lawrence exclaimed. "Here's the belt."

Jack saw the buckle end of the belt dangling in the air beside him. He reached around slowly with both hands, grasped it tightly, and took a quick breath as he called, "All right, I have it!" Then he felt himself being pulled up as the root tore loose from his jacket.

Other people had gathered on the trail at the top of the bluff to witness the rescue, or help if they could. A man from the group now knelt down beside Mr. Lawrence and reached his hand out to help Jack the rest of the way up.

"Thanks!" Jack stammered, looking gratefully at his father and the stranger who had helped. He moved far away from the edge of the bluff.

By now Father had stood up and brushed off his clothes. He came to his son's side and smoothed down a torn place on the back of his jacket, where the root had caught. Putting his arm around Jack's shoulder, he exclaimed, "Let's go and see what Mother has for lunch." The two of them started down the trail together.

His hands buried deep in his pockets, Jack trudged along in silence until they neared the picnic grounds. Then he suddenly looked up into his father's eyes and said, "I see what you mean now. You told me not to get too close to the edge of the bluff. And there wasn't time for me to ask 'Why?'"

2

The Gate of Pain

by Robert Bainum

When I opened my eyes after the splash, a new world lay before me. I saw trees, valleys, plains of pure white sand, green meadows of grass, blue bushes, and a host of fish—angelfish in iridescent blues, groupers, and sergeant fish with zebra stripes. And none of them seemed afraid of me—they swam close, as though I belonged there.

And that's how I felt, for with my scuba gear I was no longer a prisoner of gravity. I was perfectly balanced, with seven pounds of weight fastened to my weight belt. I could stand on my head or lie on my side with no effort at all. I could go up, down, or sideways with equal ease.

At first I was afraid to go very deep, so for about a half hour I paddled around near the surface. I swam under the boat; I watched my bubbles dance merrily to the surface as though they were musical notes. Everything was silent except for the sound of my breathing.

After 45 minutes of paddling near the surface, my confidence increased, and I began to dive 10 and 15 feet down. The colors that seemed so pretty from the top became even more vivid, so I went deeper. When I got down about 30 feet, I wanted to pick one of the beautiful, lavender-blue bushes, so I put my feet on the bottom. I tried to walk, but I was like a man on the moon. I would take a step and bounce, because I no longer had weight. So I went topside and put one more pound of weight onto my weight belt.

I went back again, broke off that bush, and brought it up. Underneath the water it appeared to be two feet wide by three feet high, but when I got it up and handed it to the people in the boat, it turned out to be one third that size. The clear water had acted as a magnifying glass.

I was disappointed, so I dived again, 33 feet this time. Suddenly I began feeling pain in my ears—tremendous pain. I realized I was in "the gate of pain," as divers call that terrible sensation when the ears begin to hurt.

For every foot a diver goes underwater, 65 pounds of additional pressure hit the body. Eardrums are very sensitive and may burst under even slight change of pressure. So divers must equalize this pressure change by swallowing or by snorting in their mask. Somewhere on the way down I had forgotten this rule.

Now I was standing on the bottom. I was so close to getting the beautiful piece of coral I'd come for, and all I had to do was bend my head down one more foot. But I was in "the gate of pain," and going down even one more foot would be breaking a rule. I was supposed to paddle toward the surface a few feet, thus reducing the pressure, then blow through my nose and clear my ears so the pressure would equalize. After that I could go on, deeper.

Carelessly I said to myself, "I have only one more foot. It won't matter this time." So I stooped over—and it happened!

I heard a sound like a hissing in my ear. It seemed as though it lasted a full minute. Then cold water hit my inner ear. I became dizzy, dropped the tool with which I was breaking off the coral, released that extra one-pound weight, and started topside as fast as I could go.

Then I remembered. I was breaking another rule. People who surface too fast have died. The compressed air in a diver's lungs is under great pressure, and if the diver comes up even five or six feet without exhaling, that air in their lungs—which is expanding for every foot they come up—will rupture the small blood vessels, and they may drown in their own blood.

I must slow down and breathe out—or commit suicide. Up I paddled, slowly now, exhaling the whole time. I came to the side of the boat, and friendly hands pulled me aboard. I was dizzy for 15 or 20 minutes, and my ear hurt. That evening I visited a doctor, and he told me that I had put a hole in my eardrum the size of a pinpoint.

I came home from that vacation with a new perspective—and not just of the underwater world. I realized how many times in life we get into "the gate of pain" or "the gate of temptation." We know something is wrong, yet we won't back up. While diving I learned that if we will just take time, when we are tempted, to back up a bit and study the situation—take time for the pressure of good angels to offset the pressure of bad angels and equalize the situation—we will keep ourselves out of a lot of trouble.

3

The Parrot That Preached

by Dorothy Aitken

Polly liked to sit on her perch, preen her red and green feathers, and come and go through the unscreened window. Several years before, her master had found her in the jungle and brought her home as a pet for his family.

As a young parrot, Polly had learned to imitate what she heard. About that time a white launch had glided up to the wharf on the Amazon near where Polly and her family lived. The captain and his wife had come ashore and treated all of the sick people. Afterward they had shown pictures and talked about Jesus. Polly's master had been impressed, and after several months of studying the Bible, he and his family got baptized.

Now Polly's master no longer wasted his time at the wharf with the other men, playing cards, gambling, and drinking. Instead, he worked hard cultivating his cassava plantation and taking care of his family's needs.

Polly noticed the change right away. Every Friday as her master's wife dusted Polly's perch, she would say to the bird, "*Vamos preparar a casa. Amanha é sábado.*" ("Let's prepare the house. Tomorrow is the Sabbath.")

Sometimes Polly would ride on her master's shoulder down to the wharf. She noticed that instead of stopping to play cards as he used to do, her master would say to his old cronies, "*É um pecado jogar baralho.*" ("It's a sin to play cards.")

Gradually Polly began to imitate the conversations around her. One day, as the wife was preparing to dust Polly's perch, Polly surprised her by giving a few croaks, blinking her beady eyes, and then saying in a clear voice, "*Vamos preparar a casa. Amanha é sábado.*"

The woman thought this was great fun. When her husband came home she just had to show Polly off to him. So she took her duster and walked toward Polly's perch. Immediately Polly began, "*Vamos preparar a casa. Amanha é sábado.*" Then when she saw how funny everyone thought it was, she shrilled, "*Vamos preparar a casa. Amanha a lancha virá.*" ("Let's prepare the house. Tomorrow the launch will come.") The shrieks of laughter that followed sent her into another fit of talking. "*Jogar é pecado! Jogar é pecado!*" ("Gambling is a sin.")

So Polly learned the conversation of an Adventist home.

No one knows why Polly suddenly decided to leave and fly away upstream to another village. Maybe she was out on a "fly about" and got lost; maybe she just wanted to see more of the world; or could it be that the angels led her?

At any rate, Polly flew into a tree near a small hut on the river and sat quietly blinking her eyes and looking in through an open window. Yes, there was a parrot perch. Most houses on the Amazon had one. She must find out first if there was another parrot that claimed this perch. So she sat quietly all day. She saw nothing of any other parrot, so toward evening she flew through the window and took her place on the perch.

"Oh," squealed the youngsters when they saw her. "Look, Mother! A parrot! And he's even prettier than Pedro was. Oh, Mother, may we keep him?"

By now the children were petting Polly. She didn't mind. Not even when they called her Pedro. All she wanted was a perch and something to eat.

"We'll have to see," Mother answered cautiously. She knew the parrot must belong to someone. "We will inquire whether anyone has lost a parrot. If no one claims him, I suppose we can keep him. He seems to have chosen us."

No one in the village claimed the new parrot. It seemed strange to Mother, for parrots don't usually wander very far from home after they are tamed.

The first time this woman picked up the duster and began cleaning things up a bit, Polly remembered her old home and the conversation she always had with the woman there. "*Vamos preparar a casa. Amanha é sábado.*"

"What is that you are saying, Pedro?" the woman asked. She came closer to the perch in the hope that the bird would talk again.

"Vamos preparar a casa. Amanha a lancha virá."

What a strange thing for a parrot to say, Mother thought as she picked up her duster and continued her work. Again and again Polly repeated her strange message. When Father and the children came in to eat, Polly was coaxed to show off for them. No one could understand just what she was talking about, but that didn't seem to bother Polly in the least. She kept repeating her little speech as long as anyone would listen.

Later on in the week a group of men gathered on the front porch to play cards. Immediately Polly went into action. *"Jogar é pecado!"* she screeched. *"Jogar é pecado!"*

All of the men stopped to puzzle over this strange bird. Finally, when Polly could not be silenced, her master took her into the house and put her into a cage and covered her up. He didn't like to hear her condemning words, and he was sure his friends all thought he was crazy for having such a bird in his house.

For weeks Polly kept up her evangelistic campaign, preaching in a shrill voice her strange message.

One day some of the men got to talking about her. "Maybe she belongs to that white launch that comes by here once in a while," one of the men said. "You remember, they brought us some medicine one time when we were all sick."

"Yeah, could be," added another. "I know they have some funny ideas about religion—keep Saturday for Sunday and don't drink. They probably don't dance, or smoke, or gamble with cards, either."

"Next time they come by, you should wave a white shirt or something," another friend suggested. "They'll stop to see if you are sick, and you can give them their parrot."

So Polly's master kept close watch on the river. He really wanted to get rid of that bird preacher. His conscience was bothering him about the card playing. He hated to be reminded of his sin every time he sat down to play.

Sure enough, one day the *Luzeiro* appeared around the bend, its white hull glistening in the sun. Polly's master ran quickly for something white. Then hurrying down to the riverbank, he vigorously waved it back and forth till the launch turned in his direction.

"What's the trouble here?" the captain called when he was close enough to be heard. "Someone sick?"

"Come on up close. I've got something that belongs to you," the man called back. Puzzled, the captain turned off the engine, and the launch drifted closer to the shore. The gangplank was put down, the captain picked up his medical bag, and he and the nurse stepped ashore.

Polly's master was a bit embarrassed. "I'm sorry to bother you, sir. No one is ill as far as I know. But tell me, do you prepare the house the day before your Sabbath?"

The captain took off his cap and scratched his head. "Why, yes, of course."

"Do you believe it is a sin to gamble?"

"Yes, I do."

"Then, sir, I have your bird."

"You have my what?" asked the captain, a puzzled expression on his face.

"Your bird. You know, the parrot that you lost."

"But I've never had a parrot," the captain answered. "I haven't the slightest idea what you are talking about."

"Go get the parrot," the man commanded his son. "He must be your parrot, sir. We don't know anyone else along the river who thinks it is a sin to gamble with cards, or who prepares his house for the Sabbath. It has to be your bird."

By now quite a crowd had gathered. All were watching to see what the outcome would be. Soon the boy and the parrot arrived. "Make him talk," the father commanded.

So Polly began, "*Vamos preparar a casa. Amanha é sábado. Vamos preparar a casa. Amanha a lancha virá.*" Then realizing she was showing off to a big audience, Polly screamed, "*Jogar é pecado! Jogar é pecado! Ha, ha, ha.*"

"It's plain to see that she belongs to an Adventist family somewhere along this river," the captain said. He turned to his nurse-wife. "Do you know anyone with a parrot that talks?"

"We-l-l, yes, I think I do. Don't you remember that family in the next village downstream? They used to have one. Maybe it belongs to them."

The captain took Polly, and the crowd dispersed. But the man who had brought the parrot hung around the launch till everyone was gone. Then sheepishly he asked the captain if he could talk to him alone. The captain helped him up the gangplank, and for a long time they sat discussing the things Polly had been talking about.

Every time after that when the captain passed in his launch, he would stop and give a Bible study to this interested man and his family. In time the whole family was baptized.

And Polly? She was welcomed back with open arms to her original home. She still sits on her perch and screams, "*Vamos preparar a casa. Amanha é sábado. Jogar é pecado! Ha, ha, ha.*"

4

Double Discovery

by Paulette Witt

"Paulette, where is Mrs. Snyder? We can't find her anywhere!"

Mom ran a nursing home. Mrs. Snyder was one of the home's patients, and I had been told to keep an eye on her. The sound of Mother's worried voice jerked me back to reality. I threw my book onto my bed and dived for my sneakers.

Don't tell me Mrs. Snyder's run off again! I thought as I pulled the sneakers on and dashed for the top of the stairs. *This will make the third time in one week that I've had to go chasing after that silly woman. Old people give me a headache!*

I took the steps three at a time and screeched to a halt at the bottom. My mom was standing there with her nurse's uniform on, and her countenance bore an alarming expression of question and accusation and concern. I knew I was in deep trouble, and the thought struck me that perhaps I was going to be placed under another two-week ban from my books. To me that was a punishment like medieval torture. My mother's next words, however, changed my selfish concern into genuine fear, not for myself, but for Mrs. Snyder.

"We've searched all over the building, and she is not here. Your father has been driving up and down the road looking for her. She has really disappeared this time! Probably she's wandered off into the woods somewhere." Mom gazed out the window at the lawn, still fresh and green from a recent shower. Then her eyes traveled to the tall maple and pine trees that border our property. Suddenly she turned and looked sternly at me. "Where have you been, young lady?"

"I—er—I was . . . Well, I thought she was sitting on the front porch. You know Mrs. Snyder. Never can make up her mind. She told me she was going to rest awhile."

I began to feel on the defensive. After all, my looking after her hadn't been my idea. What 13-year-old girl *would* relish the "privilege" of traipsing about the countryside on a hot summer day listening to the foolish jabbering of a senile old nursing-home patient? I was beginning to feel almost justified in my neglect of duty when my father came striding through the back door wearing an expression that brought to my mind certain unpleasant experiences in my past.

"We've got to search the woods," he said, glancing at Mother. "The boys have already started looking in the wooded area back of Mrs. Hill's pasture." He turned to me. "You're going to have to help your brothers and me. You take the section to the right of the house, and I'll go down toward Pine Creek. I hope she doesn't get that far. The current is swift, especially just before the stream rounds the bend to the bottom of the hill. I'm going to look there first."

I could tell by the deep wrinkles across his high forehead that he was worried, and his eyes seemed sad. He was disappointed in me. I remembered that this was not the first time I had let him down. Somehow, though, my failure had never seemed so serious before.

It was decided that Mom should stay behind to help care for the rest of the patients. Running a nursing home is a 24-hour job, even with plenty of hired help. Unfortunately, we had had a shortage of nurses that summer, and for this reason I had been given the responsibility of seeing that Mrs. Snyder, an eccentric, confused, but very active woman, did not wander off by herself.

It was at the beginning of the summer that I had started my new job, and at first I had not minded it. Mrs. Snyder was an amusing person, the more so because her natural oddness was accentuated by her feebleness of memory and reasoning ability. She liked to wear a big hat with a wild-looking feather sticking from it, two or three necklaces of fake pearls and tarnished silver, several bracelets on each arm, a fat crocodile-skin pocketbook, and high heels. I often wondered how she managed to move with all that extra baggage clanking about her. But move she did—with great speed!

For a while I had comforted myself with the hope that Mrs. Snyder's passion for walking was just a passing fancy. Surely no 68-year-old woman could find in hiking life's ultimate pleasure! It did not make sense to me, but I soon learned that Mrs. Snyder never made sense.

More times than I cared to remember I had plodded up and down the winding country road that passed in front of the huge brick mansion my parents had converted into a nursing home. After two weeks I was convinced that should I ever become blind, I could still walk three miles along that road without a wrong step. Boredom didn't begin to describe what I felt.

Mrs. Snyder, however, never seemed to remember having been over any particular road before. Some days she thought we were headed for "the city." Other days she believed we were going to visit her grandmother who lived "at the corner of Maple and Vine in Sunbury." Even when we changed directions, we were still going to the same place, and in her mixed-up mind she was always just a few hundred yards from her destination. I suppose that if I had been more mature, I would have felt sorry for her. Instead, I felt sorry for myself.

But now that Mrs. Snyder was really lost, my feelings, my whole attitude toward her, began to change. Looking behind trees and peering under bushes, I made my hurried way through the thick Pennsylvania forest. All the time I was thinking of how terrible it would be if we didn't find her before darkness came, or worse still, if we didn't find her at all. In my imagination I could see her tripping and breaking her leg or falling into the creek and drowning. She had no sense of direction, so there was no hope of her ever finding her way out of this dark tangle of woods.

"Dear God, please lead us to Mrs. Snyder," I prayed as I ran ahead, stumbling over fallen limbs and scratching myself on dead pine branches. "Please don't let anything happen to her. It was my duty to watch her, and if any harm comes to her, it will be my fault. Forgive me, please, for failing in my duty. I know I've had the wrong attitude toward her and my responsibility, but I realize my mistake now. I will not be selfish any longer."

How could I have been so lazy and thoughtless, I wondered, *as to consider only my own comfort and convenience?* My parents had depended on me, but I had proved unworthy. Would they ever believe in me again? And Mrs. Snyder had needed me, even if she had not realized it. I had not realized it myself until just then, but it was becoming clearer to me with each step I took that I had not merely been given a job to do—I had been given the responsibility for another human being's safety. How I hoped that my failure would not result in tragedy!

On and on I plunged. When at the edge of a clearing I almost ran into one of the neighbor's cows, I stopped short. Into my mind flashed an incident that had taken place just the day before.

While passing our neighbor's farm, Mrs. Snyder had noticed one of his beef cows peacefully grazing beside the fence. "Look at that big black bear!" she had exclaimed. "We must get a gun!" Off she had gone like a soldier in full retreat. (I have never been able to figure out how she could cover the ground so quickly in those heels of hers.)

Running to catch her, I had laughingly explained that her "bear" was only a Black Angus heifer. Now I found myself wondering what she would do if she really did meet a bear. Not that it was likely, but to me in my state of mind almost anything seemed likely.

I searched for nearly five hours, scouring the area like a detective, which, indeed, I practically was; but not a trace did I find of my truant. It was less than an hour until sundown when I finally turned my leaden feet toward home.

The last rays of the afternoon sun were tipping the treetops with gold, and the air was vibrant with the sound of the wood thrushes' evening lullaby. Somehow, though, the songs did not seem as cheerful as usual. The heaviness of my heart kept me from sharing in their joy over a day successfully completed. Dejection oozed from every pore of my weary body.

As I limped along, my every step became a prayer that Mrs. Snyder would be at the house when I got there. Maybe my brothers or my father had found her. My feet gained speed from this thought, and soon I was hurrying up the gravel driveway. There on the front lawn stood my brother Maurice.

"Look what I found," he called as I came closer. "It's Mrs. Snyder's sweater." Indeed it was her sweater, torn and dirty. But where was Mrs. Snyder? Maurice had not seen her. By this time I was becoming nearly frantic.

I heard voices in the backyard. Looking up, I saw Father just rounding the corner of the house, leading a bedraggled and much subdued Mrs. Snyder. Tears of joy filled my eyes as I ran to meet them.

"I discovered her lying on the ground under a pine tree, snoring like a lumberjack," Dad said, and he laughed. I could tell that he was relieved too.

Mrs. Snyder started up the steps, and I took her arm to help her. "Madam, I am at your service!" I said, and I smiled across at Dad, who was holding the other arm. I noticed that the wrinkles in his forehead were gone.

Then he looked at me with a new expression in his eyes. He had read the change that had taken place in my heart during those five long hours of searching. He knew that I had discovered something too, something of great importance.

5

Snakes on the River

by Kevin D. Ippisch

The kink in my back made me feel as if I'd slept on a stump. Reaching over to the corner of the tent, I grabbed my clothes. They felt cold and damp. I stuffed them into my sleeping bag with me to warm them up, but they gave me goose bumps, so I decided just to get up. I crawled out of the bag, slipped into my pants and shirt, and added a sweatshirt.

"Where are you going?" I had wakened Dennis, and now he was looking at me through sleepy eyes.

"Just outside to walk around," I said.

Unzipping the door of the tent, I stuck my head out. The cold chill went right through me, but I went out anyway.

Elder Westfall, one of our youth leaders, called, "Kevin, will you help me collect wood to start a fire?"

"OK," I replied.

Once we had gotten the fire going, I stood next to it

to warm up. The toes of my tennis shoes were damp from the dew, so I held each one over the fire alternately. The camp began to stir, and people joined me at the fire.

Soon my mother was helping the rest of the women fix breakfast. She was having a good time, but it embarrassed me to have her along on our youth canoe trip. I remembered when she had first told me she was going to come.

"Mom," I had said heatedly, "why do you have to go? The trip is for us kids. Can't you just stay home and let me have some fun by myself?"

"But I already told Elder Westfall that I'd go along as a chaperone if he needed me." She had said it almost apologetically. "I asked him to try to get somebody else if he could, but he said he'd already asked everyone." Then she had added, "Dennis' mother is going too, so you won't be suffering alone."

After breakfast we struck camp and headed down the river. Since Dennis and I were about the last ones to leave, most of the others were strung out ahead of us. We made good time, though; the current was swift, and we were both pretty good canoeists. Before long we started catching up with the others.

A short distance ahead I saw the canoe with my mother and her canoeing partner. As we gained on them, I watched their inexperienced paddling. My mother was having a terrible time trying to steer. She'd paddle a few strokes on one side, then change sides and paddle on the other side a few strokes. Each time she'd change sides, water from her paddle would drip into the canoe. *It serves her right for coming—to have a bit of a rough time*, I thought.

As we passed them, Mom called over to me, "Having a good time? I hope so."

I was glad no one but Dennis was around to hear. His mother was along too, so I didn't worry about him; but I hated for any of the other kids to get the impression that I was tied to my mother's apron strings.

At noon we stopped for lunch. The sun was high and hot then, and everyone seemed in good spirits. After lunch Dennis' mother called us over. She first looked sternly at me and said, "Your poor mother has had a terrible time canoeing. You should see the blisters on her hands." Then she turned to Dennis. "I haven't had it very easy either. It won't hurt you boys to canoe with your mothers awhile." There was a note of finality in her voice that didn't allow argument.

As we walked down to the canoes I grumbled to Dennis, "It sure is going to be bad news canoeing with our mothers."

After my mom boarded the canoe, I pushed us off. Wanting to help, Mom tried to steer the canoe from the front, but that made it twice as hard for me to steer from the back. Finally I got exasperated and said, "Why don't you just let me paddle for a while, Mom? I think it'll be easier that way."

Dennis was having similar problems, so we stayed close together. The rest of the canoes, however, disappeared down the river.

Seeing that I was a bit ahead of him, Dennis tried to catch up, but I wasn't about to let him. Soon we were racing. I was paddling as hard as I could, trying to keep the lead; he was paddling furiously to catch me.

Ahead of us loomed a bend in the river and a small island of dead branches and debris. I headed for the wider channel, which was on the right. I was just about at the bend when Dennis caught up with me.

"Look out, Dennis!" I heard his mother scream, but it was too late.

He hit the back end of our canoe, changing our direction and heading us directly toward the small island. The swift current didn't give me time to steer away, and our canoe slammed up on a partially submerged log on the left side of the island. Branches from trees on the island hung over our canoe.

Suddenly Mom screamed. A snake as big around as a handle of a canoe paddle had fallen out of a branch and was crawling up the side of the canoe next to her. When I looked up to see why she had screamed, I found myself looking into the repulsive face of another snake on an overhanging branch. Its black beady eyes were staring straight at me, and its brown body hung above the canoe as if it would drop into it at any second. Looking past it, I saw that the rest of the branches were covered with snakes.

Mother batted her snake back into the water with her canoe paddle and frantically tried to push away from the island. I wedged my paddle against something under the water and put my face against my shoulder to brace myself. Then I pushed away as hard as I could, my heart pounding as loud as a stampede of elephants.

Slowly the canoe slid off the log and back into deeper water. We were free from the island, but I found that my face was stuck to my shoulder. The braces on my teeth had hooked on my shirt and wouldn't come loose.

Both Mom and I were drained of strength, and I was hampered by my tooth-to-shoulder position, so we made our way down the river quite slowly, just letting the current take us. Not far down, Dennis and his mother were waiting.

"What on earth happened to you?" Mrs. Phillips exclaimed as we pulled in to shore.

Mom explained as we worked at unhooking my braces. "We got stuck on a log next to the island . . . and a huge snake started crawling into the canoe next to me. I was so scared I didn't know what to do, and poor Kevin had a snake hanging right in front of his face!" The way she told it, it sounded like the most exciting thing that had ever happened.

After I was unhooked and we had rested a few minutes, we were ready to start on our way again. Before we shoved off, Mom said, "If you want, you and Dennis can canoe together again. I think Mrs. Phillips and I can make it."

"That's OK, Mom," I said. "I've changed my mind—it's really quite enjoyable canoeing with you. Come on, let's see what new excitement we can find."

6

Help!

by Peggy Hodges

"Hey, Brad, what are you doing in Mr. Watson's boat?" Greg called. "That's strictly off-limits, you know."

"Don't worry about it. Mr. Watson was called back to the city to tend to some important business, and he asked me to keep an eye on his boat while he was gone."

"I bet you're not supposed to run it, though. You know how fussy he is about the thing."

"Just checking out the engine." Brad winked at his friend. "Got to keep it in shape, you know. I think I'll take a spin around the bay and see if it's performing right."

"May I go? I've never been out in a big boat like that. The *Sea Queen* is a regular yacht!"

"Naw, Mr. Watson wouldn't like it."

"Please! I won't touch anything," Greg persisted.

"Forget it. I'll just be gone a short time. I'll be back

in time to go to the big Indian barbecue with you. I sure don't want to miss that."

Brad started the engine and waved at Greg, who stood forlornly on the dock. "See you later!"

He backed away and headed the boat into the bay. The bright sunshine made dazzling ripples on the water as he tilted the boat into a curve. He loved the smooth steering and the purr of the big inboard. He had the bay all to himself and opened the throttle wide, enjoying the quick response of the big boat. It was the first time he had been on it alone.

A little twinge of conscience stirred him, but he resisted it. Mr. Watson was fussy about his boat, but Brad was sure that if he'd asked whether he could take it out, the answer would have been "Go ahead." After all, the boat had every safety device required and had passed a rigid Coast Guard inspection. And Mr. Watson had often allowed Brad to steer the *Sea Queen* when they went fishing. There was nothing to worry about.

I'll go out a little way and then turn around, Brad decided. *When I get back, I'll go right over to the barbecue and meet Greg. That's where I told my folks I was going.*

Brad leaned back in his seat as he skimmed over the waves. When he saw the torpedo-like log looming in the water, it was too late. He hit it head-on, and it ripped through the shining mahogany of the boat. A loud boom rang in Brad's ears as he crashed into the side of the boat, his leg twisting under him.

He lay there dazed for a few moments. Then a movement of the careening vessel catapulted him overboard, and the pressure of the water seemed to explode in his head. He flailed his arms and rose to the surface. In spite of the pain throbbing in his right leg, he desperately treaded water and looked at the distant outline of the shore.

He tried to think, but his brain was slow to respond. How far was he from shore? He figured maybe two miles, and he was thankful he was a good swimmer. But how far could he swim with his leg injured? Maybe he had broken it.

Everything had happened so fast that he couldn't believe it. A few minutes before, he had been full of an exhilarating sense of power as he steered the beautiful boat, and now he was in the ocean, aching and benumbed.

He looked for the *Sea Queen*. It seemed far away, but he determinedly swam toward it. It took a long time to get close to it. What he saw made him sick. The boat was almost completely underwater and sinking fast.

Gritting his teeth, he dived for the whiteness of a life belt shining through the roily water and pulled downward on it. Then he tried yanking upward to release it from the boat. But it was no use. The clamp was too tight. He couldn't budge it.

The log that had done all the damage was floating nearby. He swam to it and tried to slide over it, but it was so water-soaked that it gave no more support than a bottle cork. He sank, swallowing a mouthful of salty water. Struggling to the surface again, he tried to hold on to the soggy log, but it rolled over, tipping him into the water again. He tried a few more times, but then gave up. It was no use.

He shook his head and tried to think what to do.

I have to do the right thing now, he realized frantically. *I've already messed up on some of the most important rules of boating. Here I am, without even a life jacket. And there are 12 of them on the* Sea Queen!

These thoughts didn't make him feel any better. Mr. Watson allowed no one on his boat without a life jacket. That was a must. The first thing he did when he took people out was hand them each a life jacket.

But I was going for such a short ride, Brad thought. He knew that was no excuse as he wryly compared it to the one given by people who didn't fasten their seat belts because they were just driving "around the block." He couldn't excuse his actions—he just regretted the carelessness with which he had jumped into the *Sea Queen* and headed into the bay.

He stared at the setting sun that was turning the shoreline a deep red. Treading water, he wondered whether to try to make shore or rest on his back, hoping for a boat to come along. Soon it would be too dark for anyone to see him. No, his best course would be to head for shore. His leg felt better, so he decided it wasn't broken after all. He kicked his shoes off and wiggled out of his wet jeans. There, that felt better!

At least he wasn't hungry. He was thankful for the big

lunch his mother had made him eat before he left. Thankful, too, for his good health and the swimming lessons that, combined with his husky build, made him a strong swimmer. If the shore actually was two miles away, it would take at least six hours of swimming to reach it, maybe more.

He tried a relaxed breaststroke, thinking it would be the least tiring. But he just couldn't seem to get the right response from his muscles and made very little progress. Every few hundred feet he rolled over on his back to rest and to think his disturbing thoughts.

Who would search for him? Not his folks. They thought that he was over where Greg's folks were camped and that he would go to the barbecue with Greg. They wouldn't be alarmed about him until the barbecue was over, and that would be 9:00 at the earliest. They'd never dream he'd be out in the *Sea Queen*.

How about Greg? There was little hope there, either. No doubt Greg had gone to the barbecue with his folks, thinking that Brad would be along later. If he didn't show up, Greg wouldn't be alarmed, for it wouldn't be the first time Brad had failed to do what he promised.

How he wished he had allowed Greg to come with him! If Greg had been along, one of them probably would have seen the log and given the familiar warning: "Deadhead dead ahead!" Most of all he wished he had never taken Mr. Watson's boat.

He forced himself to paddle on. It was dark now, and he could see faint lights from the few houses along the shore. But never a boat. He knew he was gaining only a few yards and cautioned himself to stay calm and not panic. Thirst racked his throat, but he steeled himself not to drink the salty water. His eyes felt puffy and stung.

He realized how small and unimportant he was out on that large body of water. He knew that only God could help him now, and he was almost ashamed to ask for His help. Finally, though, he closed his eyes and prayed, asking forgiveness and renewing his pledge to be faithful.

A bright moon turned the dark water an eerie silver, and he knew it was late—very late. He lay back in the water and rested awhile. A hard object hit the back of his head, and he turned in fright. It was a buoy! He slid his chest awkwardly over it and hung on. The horrible events of the afternoon crowded through his mind again, and the realization that he had brought them on himself was the worst. He remembered Greg's wistful look as the boat had pulled out from the dock and Mr. Watson's trust when he'd asked Brad to look after the *Sea Queen*.

He remembered a lot of other things, too. *How can I be all that rotten and still have everyone be so good to me?* he thought. *I've been treated with kindness, trust, and affection, but have given so little in return.*

"If I ever get back to shore, I'll be different," he said aloud. He shut his eyes and wept.

Just then a bright beacon of light shone through his closed eyelids, and he opened them to see a boat pulling up. It was the Coast Guard!

On the trim little cutter were his folks, Greg's folks, and Greg.

"I knew you were in trouble when you didn't show up at the barbecue," Greg said. "I waited for a while, and then I told my folks. They were worried too, so they went over to your cabin. When your dad and mom learned that you had gone out in the *Sea Queen*, they were afraid you had had trouble with the engine. So they called the Coast Guard. We're sure glad you're all right. We've been searching for hours."

Brad shook violently as they lifted him from the water and wrapped warm blankets around him. He reached out to Greg and grabbed his hand.

"The Lord showed you the way to help me, Greg. But the *Sea Queen*—it's completely gone! Oh, Dad! Oh, Mom!" He sobbed uncontrollably.

"Don't think about that now, son," Dad said. "Mr. Watson probably has insurance to cover his loss. If not, we'll take care of it some way. The important thing is that you're safe."

"The *Sea Queen* is replaceable, but you aren't," Mom said as she kissed his tired face. "Just rest now. We'll soon be home."

Reassured by their love, Brad fell into the deep sleep of exhaustion.

Mom turned to Greg. "Well, Greg," she said, "I'm sure you'll have a very different friend in Brad when he wakes up."

7

The Glory Hole

by Henry S. Jones

The pickup truck bucked and jumped like a rodeo bronco. In the back our sleeping bags and other gear would have jumped out if they hadn't been tied down.

"Uncle Bob, are you sure you haven't run off the road?" I asked.

Uncle Bob just grinned and held tight to the steering wheel.

My older brother, Wade, who had been up there before, never let me forget it. "I told you, Buck, that we'd be roughing it."

I was happy anyway. We were going to spend two weeks at Uncle Bob's gold mine. A real gold mine! I breathed hard every time I thought of it. I could scarcely wait to find a nugget, maybe two.

A few minutes later the road ended at a hillside. Wooden shacks perched on the side of the hill like eagles' nests. Then I stared, openmouthed. Surely this wasn't the mine!

"Why, it's just a little hole in the side of the mountain," I exclaimed. "Can you really see the gold the miners bring out?" I tried to sound casual, but I was itching to find gold for myself.

Uncle Bob gave me a strange look. "It takes experience, Buck. And those miners in there have to remember that it's *my* gold."

My face burned. I had been hoping that if we found some nuggets somewhere on the mountain trails, Uncle Bob would let us keep them.

"Uncle Bob," Wade said, "the last time I was here I saw lots of old tunnels dug into the hill. May we explore some of them?"

Uncle Bob stopped the truck and got out. "I want you boys to listen good now. You stay out of those old diggings. They're full of death traps. Stay out of them! Do you understand?"

I had never seen Uncle Bob so serious. Wade and I both nodded, but I couldn't give up the idea of finding some gold somewhere, maybe even locating a new vein. Perhaps then Uncle Bob would let me keep one or two nuggets.

Wade and I watched the miners in their rubber rain gear and hard hats with electric lights on them. The men pushed the ore cars to the dump and unloaded them by tripping a lever. I looked in one of the cars, but couldn't see any gold. The miners assured us there actually was gold in the rock.

A few days later I was looking around in the ore house and found an old carbide miner's lamp. I was fascinated with it. "How does it work?" I asked Uncle Bob.

"Oh, that's Old Smokey. It really lets out the smoke." He explained that carbide is highly explosive if it gets wet, and showed me how the lamp worked. He put a few rocks in the bottom of the lamp and some water in the top, adjusting the water flow so that water dripped off the end of the rod that extended into the carbide holder. Then he slapped his hand flat against the face of the lamp and with a quick motion struck a spark from the lighter. The lamp popped, and a bright flame showed through the smoke. "You see, it works fine, even if it does smoke. Look it over." He turned back to some old blueprints he had been looking at.

"What are those for, Uncle Bob?"

"Huh? Oh, these. They are the only known records of the many tunnels in this hill, all in the quest for gold."

I looked at a map. There was a note in red: "Danger. Low set."

"What's a low set, Uncle Bob?"

"Oh, that's where the miners stopped a cave-in from overhead. Most of the tunnels in this area are through solid rock. However, when there's danger of a cave-in, some areas have wood shoring. I'm sure you boys won't ever see a low set. But if you do, don't go under it."

Two days later I convinced Wade that we should look for nuggets up on the mountain. Wade took his big, handheld electric lantern, and I carried my new five-cell flashlight. Just for the fun of it, I stopped by the ore house and borrowed Old Smokey. I put new carbide in, but left the water out.

We scrambled up the mountain in search of an open vein on the surface and stumbled onto an old mine tunnel.

Wade's eyes shone with gold fever. "Shall we give it a try?" he half whispered.

I didn't have to be persuaded. I was even more feverish than Wade.

The mine was very old. A musty smell drifted out of the opening, and the walls were wet. About 100 feet inside we came to a low set, the very kind of wooden shoring Uncle Bob had told me about. Wade wanted to go back, but I'd gone too far now to turn back. I could almost see gold nuggets, and I wanted one more than anything in the world.

Wade got down on his hands and knees and pointed his light at the supports holding up the low set. "See that, Buck? The wood is rotten."

"So what? If we don't touch the wood, we can crawl through on our hands and knees." I added for good measure, "Don't be a scaredy-cat."

We crawled through, Wade first. My head was out the other side of the shoring when something on my belt snagged a rock. Without thinking, I jerked on ahead.

That's when the mine ceiling crashed down around us with a thundering roar. Falling debris knocked my flashlight out of my hand. Wade lost his grip on his lantern, and the light went out.

"Are you all right, Buck?" Wade's voice trembled. It sounded the way I felt—scared to death.

I couldn't see a thing. I never believed there could be such heavy darkness. The only sound was our breathing and the water that dripped from overhead.

"Buck, you hear me? Are you OK?"

"Yes, I think so. I can't tell for sure. Can you find your light?"

"Yeah. Here it is." He flicked on the switch and shone the light on the rockslide. The low set we had crawled under was completely buried. The tunnel was closed solid.

"What are we going to do, Wade? With the tunnel closed, we'll smother long before anybody finds us."

"No, we don't have to worry about air. This mine has so many cracks to the outside that the tunnels don't need any ventilators."

I looked around for my flashlight but couldn't find it. "Well, I guess I'll never see that flashlight again."

"What about Old Smokey?"

"Oh, sure." I felt my belt at the back. "That's what got hung up when I crawled through the low set." I took Old Smokey from my belt. "We need water."

Wade grunted. "What's this wet stuff falling on us?"

I remembered Uncle Bob's demonstration, and in a few minutes Old Smokey was in business. Then came the smoke. I held the light out to the side so the smoke wouldn't blind me. Wade beamed his light ahead to a dark hole. Across the hole an ore car stood at a crazy angle. The tracks ahead of it hung into the black hole. The tunnel floor was gone except for a narrow ledge that slipped off to nothing before it reached the other side.

"What's that hole doing there?" I asked Wade.

"That's called a glory hole. When they find a rich vein they follow it down as far as it goes." He picked up a rock about the size of a grapefruit. "Let's listen for the bottom." He threw the rock out toward the center of the hole. It hit a track, then continued on down in silence. Then a faint splash echoed up to us.

"Will we have to cross it?" I was scared.

"Yes, and it's 300 feet deep if it's an inch." Wade looked pale-white through the dirt. I'm sure I looked that way too. I knew without question that we had to cross the glory hole if we expected to get out of that tunnel alive.

"Wade, before we start across that hole, let's pray."

We took turns praying until we were calm enough to make the treacherous jump across the almost-bottomless glory hole.

Wade went first, and landed well on the other side. "Boy, does this feel good." I could hear his breath come in deep sobs.

As for me, I was losing interest in crossing that hole,

but I knew I'd better cross while I still had some nerve. With Old Smokey in my left hand, I inched out on the ledge. "Let's see some light, Wade."

He shone the light on my feet, but I was afraid to look down.

"Buck, you have to watch where you're going."

"OK. But I don't want to look into that dark hole." I made a final prayer and jumped.

I landed a little past Wade. Then we both knelt in thanksgiving. But we didn't feel elated long. Just around the corner we came to the face of the tunnel. The face is the end, and that is what we were sure we now faced.

Wade and I slumped down on some big rocks. I looked at Old Smokey. It was really putting out the smoke.

"When do you suppose they'll find us?" I quavered. I watched the smoke from my lamp. It trailed up behind some big boulders.

Suddenly I jumped up. "Wade, shine your light up that trail of smoke."

"That's where our fresh air is coming from," Wade explained. "Let's see where that is."

We climbed up over the boulders and found a big, long hole going upward. "That's the stope hole," Wade said. "It's the reverse of a glory hole."

Good Old Smokey. We followed its smoke until it seemed to melt into the rock above us. Then I noticed grass roots growing through the cracks.

"Out of the way, Wade," I shouted, putting my shoulder to the rock above and pushing. With Wade close behind, I landed on the grass outside, in the blessed sunlight.

We met Uncle Bob on the way down the mountain.

"Where have you boys been?" he asked.

Wade shrugged. "Just looking for a lost gold vein."

Uncle Bob grinned. "Find any?"

"We did better than that," I said.

"How's that?"

It was my turn to grin. "We found the sunlight. That's the most beautiful gold there is."

Then, as Uncle Bob studied us with a quizzical look on his face, I added, "We also found out what can happen when we don't mind. And best of all, we found out how God answers prayer!"

Uncle Bob didn't say anything for a long time. He just stood there scratching his head and looking down at the ground. Then he motioned for us to follow him over to an old wooden bench and drawled, "Tell me about this change in you boys."

8

Pride Ride

by Judith E. Hohensee

"How about taking these horses for one more run before supper?" That was Darby, my best friend, calling to me.

I shook my head and yelled back, "We don't have that much time left."

At that, she and her cousin Tara headed their mounts closer to my side. "Well, then, how about cantering back to the stable with us?" Tara asked. "You learned how to do that this morning."

"Nope," I responded. "I'll just walk this old horse back to the stable. You two go on ahead. I don't want to hold you back."

"Well, OK, if you want to be a baby. We'll wait for you, so try to be there before Christmas!" Darby said with a laugh, and both girls galloped off.

We had been out for a relaxed afternoon of riding on

our day off from summer camp counseling. The rolling New England hills, bright emerald in the summer sun, made a breathtaking backdrop for our afternoon recreation. We were ending a lazy day of riding up and down the camp property. We had shared all the news from home and had counted all the clouds we saw, and now we were refreshed and ready for another week of counseling. It had been a wonderful day—almost.

My problem was that I loved to ride but was just plain clumsy. I tried so hard to ride with as much style and skill as Darby and Tara, but I always ended up bouncing helplessly around like a sack of potatoes.

So I was glad to see them ride ahead. Now I could ride as slowly as I pleased. I knew my patient old mare was eager to get back home to her oats, but I kept her reined in anyway. We arrived 20 minutes later, just as my friends were starting to sweep out the stable.

"What took you so long, Liz? Still scared of letting your horse go faster than a walk? Afraid of looking dumb, aren't you?" Tara grinned as she spoke. She was only teasing, as usual. And, as usual, I teased back.

"You probably wouldn't know, but we don't do much horseback riding in New York City. Nowadays most civilized people ride in cars. But I guess you hick farmers haven't progressed that far!"

Tara threw a handful of straw at me. "Listen, you deprived city kid! I don't even know why I waste my precious time in the hopeless job of teaching you how to ride a horse! You're such a scaredy-cat that I might as well give up! I doubt you even know the difference between a saddle and your own left foot! And—" But she couldn't finish her harangue. We were both laughing too hard.

Darby spoke above our noise. "Look, will you two quit goofing around? Let's get this place cleaned up so we can get to supper. I'm starving!"

The horses had almost finished their oats as we swept up the last shreds of straw. I stood still for a minute and watched them eat. Their chestnut coats glowed in the soft amber-colored light of the late-afternoon sun. This was my favorite time of day, and the horses too seemed to sense the special calm of approaching twilight.

I patted a comfortable-looking bale of hay. "Why don't you two go on ahead to supper? I think maybe I'll sit here for a little while. I'm really worn out from all that riding."

Darby nodded, then beckoned to her cousin. "Let's leave Liz here so she can have a nice private talk with her animal pals. I want to get down to the dining hall and find out if our good director, Elder T., is taking us out for ice cream tonight like he promised."

"Yeah! I sure don't want to miss that!" agreed Tara. "And don't forget to remind me to tell Elder T. about Buck. That horse really gave me a rough time this afternoon. He looked like a gentle horse when we first bought him for my class, but I guess he was fooling us. Just like he's trying to fool us now. Look at him! He doesn't look as if he had a mean bone in his body!"

She was right. Buck nickered softly over his feed, and then, almost as if to challenge Tara's statement, he turned and looked mournfully in her direction.

She wrinkled her nose at him. "Don't give me that innocent act! I have to call up that guy who sold us these horses and see whether he'll trade Buck for another horse. I've got enough to worry about, running horsemanship class for a bunch of campers, without having to worry about unpredictable horses. Besides, I sure wouldn't want one of our kids to get hurt. At least I don't have to worry about you falling off him, Liz, since you probably wouldn't get within 10 miles of him! Come on, Darby, let's go eat before I pass out from hunger. Don't stay here too long, Liz, OK?"

The two girls jogged toward the dining hall. I watched until the dust settled behind them, and then walked over to Buck. He might be dangerous, but he was certainly a beautiful animal, with his deep-red coloring and muscled body.

"So here we are alone, old boy," I said softly. "You know, we sort of have something in common. We're both kind of out of place here. I mean, you're a wild horse with a mind of your own, and you don't belong in a stall full of kids' gentle horses. And I'm a girl who's always lived in a big city full of dirt and noise and crowds of people. Sometimes I feel so different from the others who work here at camp. Like Darby and Tara, for instance, who are so great at riding horses and hiking and building campfires. I get so jealous sometimes! I wish I could do something to show them I'm just as smart as they are. Of course, they don't mean to be better at everything. They really can't help it if they've both lived around horses and woods all their lives."

I patted Buck on the rump and watched his muscles ripple. As he idly flicked his tail, an idea popped into my mind.

"Maybe—just for practice, of course—I could put a saddle on you and a bit, too. Tara showed me how to do all that this morning. I wouldn't dare ride you, but I could just get you ready—to see whether I could do it all by myself!"

I moved to unfasten the saddle from its hook on the wall, and then hesitated. There couldn't be any harm in doing this, could there? I just had to prove to myself that I was just as capable as my two friends.

Mentally I reviewed the steps Tara had demonstrated. And then slowly, ever so carefully, I fastened the saddle on Buck. I reached for his bit and gingerly placed it in his mouth, hoping his big yellow teeth wouldn't mistake my fingers for crunchy bits of hay. Then I stepped back to survey my work.

"Well, you look pretty good to me, Buck. Too bad I'm not a state champion rider like Tara, or you and I would go for a little ride. It's just not fair that she's so good with horses—it makes me jealous when I think about it!"

I moved to undo the saddle, and then hesitated.

There really was no reason that I couldn't just sit in the saddle and imagine that I too was a champion rider. Surely that would be safe enough. Besides, nobody was around to stop me!

I thought about leaping up on Buck the way Tara and Darby mounted. But I just wasn't coordinated enough for that, so I dragged a crate over and clambered onto Buck. Settling myself in the saddle, I eased my feet into the stirrups. Buck whinnied nervously, but didn't move.

"Want to go for a ride, boy?" I murmured softly. "I know you do, and I'm sorry, but I don't dare go anywhere on you. Too bad nobody's around to see how good I look sitting here! All I need to do is grab the reins like this, and—"

I had just made a very bad mistake. Because, at the same moment I reached for the reins, Buck shot off as if someone had cracked a whip over him!

Frantically I jerked on the reins as he dashed for the stable door, and I ducked just in time, or I would have hit my head. Jerking the reins did no good, because Buck was headed for the open fields—with me flopping up and down on his back. I tried desperately to remember what Tara had told me about stopping a horse. Did she say to pull the reins in? Or was I supposed to let the reins go slack? Should I give the horse his head?

It was too late to guess. Buck suddenly wheeled to the left, and the reins whipped out of my sweating hands, leaving a burning red welt on my palm. I made a wild grab at the reins, but they trailed beyond my reach. The only thing left to hang on to was the saddle horn. I clutched it so tightly that my hands turned chalky white.

This is insane, I thought. *This is crazy! It can't be happening to me!*

And then I felt my insides twist into knots. Buck was taking me at top speed right toward the forest. Those woods were thick and full of low limbs. If Buck tried to run into the trees, I could be slashed and torn by those branches.

Hot tears streamed down my cheeks. I couldn't think of anything to do except jump off the horse before he reached the trees, but I was too terrified to move. I kept yelling at Buck, but he didn't pay any attention. What if I were cut to death or thrown off? What if I broke my neck and died? Who would find my body?

Wild thoughts flashed through my mind, until a chilling sight froze my bones—Buck wasn't running straight toward the woods. He was headed toward a gigantic, sprawling, dead oak tree, which had heavy, thick branches around the lower part of the trunk.

All I could do was pray, for there was no way I could avoid smashing into those branches, even if I ducked. And a very clear picture came into my mind—a painting that I had seen of Absalom, King David's son, hanging by his hair from a tree.

"Help me, God, please!" I screamed.

Buck veered away from the tree, but we passed so

close to it that I felt the tip of a branch brush against my forehead. And then I fainted. At least, I think I must have fainted, because the next thing I remembered was opening my eyes and seeing the now-dark sky, and underneath me I could feel cool, rough grass. Faint voices drifted around me, sounding as if they came from far, far away.

"Liz! Are you OK? Hey, say something. Wake up, please!"

I turned my head. Darby knelt by my side, looking terribly worried. Behind her stood Tara.

"What's the matter with everybody? How come I'm lying here?" I muttered.

"What's the matter?" echoed Darby as she dropped to the ground on all fours. "You've been lying there, passed out, for minutes. We saw you weren't in the stable, and then we noticed that Buck was gone too, and we figured you had taken him out for a ride. We were standing there wondering what to do when in walked old Buck, with the saddle half falling off his back."

"Yeah!" continued Tara. "And we thought you might have been dumb enough to try to ride him, so we ran out here to see whether we could find you. Boy, were we ever scared when we saw you on the ground!"

Darby squinted her eyes and looked closely at me. "How do you feel? Think you've broken any bones?"

I moved my arms and legs carefully, and then slowly sat up. "I think I'm all right. Just a little dizzy, sort of like

I've just gotten out of bed after sleeping too long. Give me a hand so I can stand up."

The girls pulled me to my feet, and as I stood, I rubbed my legs and arms just to make sure. Nothing felt bruised, and nothing hurt. I just felt groggy and had to shake my head a little to try to clear my brain. Otherwise, I felt wonderful—for someone who had just fallen off a horse, that is.

"How about telling us what happened? Maybe you don't feel like talking?" Darby frowned and then shook her head. "I know you didn't mean for your secret ride to end this way! I really thought you knew better than to go out alone—and on Buck, of all horses. Didn't you hear Tara tell us about his being dangerous?"

So I had to tell my friends the whole embarrassing story, and it made me feel really stupid. Here I was, old enough to be counseling a group of junior campers, and yet I was foolish enough to get on a horse that Tara, a state champion rider, could hardly control. And I did it all to prove something to myself. But what did I prove?

We walked slowly back to our cabins. As we walked, my mind buzzed with questions. Why was I totally unhurt after falling off that horse? Was it because I had screamed at God to help me? And why didn't I have even a little bump on me? It looked as if God had decided to relax me by having me faint, because I couldn't remember a single thing that happened after we passed that tree.

I was so wrapped up in my thoughts that I didn't pay

attention to the whispering of Tara and Darby, until suddenly Darby grabbed my arm.

"Liz, there's something wrong with your face. I think it's your eyes. Hey—that's it—you don't have any eyelashes! Here, stand under this light so we can see you better."

I touched my eyes. I couldn't feel any lashes! "Where'd they go?" I yelled so loudly I made Darby jump back.

"Hey, don't scare me like that!" she said. "I wonder what happened, Liz. Say—do you think, just maybe, that some tree branches might have torn your lashes off? But your face doesn't have any marks on it at all, except that you really look weird!"

Tara shook her head. "This is the craziest thing I've ever heard of. First you do a dumb thing like ride Buck when no one's around. Then he throws you, or you fall off, whichever, but you pass out so you don't even remember what happened, and when you wake up, you don't have a sore spot on you! And your eyelashes fell off sometime during your ride. What happened out there, Liz? Were you so scared that your eyelashes dropped off?"

For some reason that sounded so ridiculous to us that we burst out laughing. The laughing helped me relax a little, and we walked the rest of the way in silence.

As soon as I reached my room, I knelt down by the bed. My thoughts were confused, and I was desperately tired, but I knew I had to do one very important thing before I dropped off to sleep. I had to thank my patient, understanding Father in heaven, who had prevented me from really hurting myself. All I lost from the experience were my eyelashes and a lot of pride, but I gained a lot of knowledge. For the first time I really understood what King Solomon meant when he warned, "Pride goes before destruction, and a haughty spirit before a fall" (Proverbs 16:18, NKJV).

Oh, yes—my eyelashes grew back in a couple of months, but they were much too slow in coming as far as I was concerned. Everyone at camp wanted to hear what caused "Liz's funny-looking eyes." But as I told the story again and again, I came to see God's wonderful kindness to me that wild evening when He decided to teach me a life-changing lesson.

9

The Late Night Visitor

by Alta Petersen

The whole world seemed wrapped in silence. Not a leaf stirred. No cars passed on the streets. Even the birds were silent.

"H'mm, must be time to get up!" Kyla Sue Jemron, a small 6-year-old, glanced at her sleeping sister. She gently shook the other girl and said, "It's tomorrow."

Rhoda, 8 years old and much bigger, rolled over, opened one eye to the morning light, and groaned, "Hush up and go back to sleep. It's still . . . zzz . . ."

Kyla sighed, shocked that her sister hadn't appreciated being awakened. It was bad enough to have to stop play and go to bed just because it was dark. But why stay in bed when it was light and lovely out? So she didn't! After she had dressed, she slipped quietly down the stairs so as not to waken her three younger siblings.

She peeked into the kitchen. Strange. Mother was

usually fixing breakfast when she came downstairs in the morning. And Daddy wasn't reading the morning paper. She quietly opened the kitchen door and went to her favorite spot, the orchard.

She climbed a cherry tree at the edge of the orchard and swung by her knees from the lower branch. The grass beneath her looked like a thick green carpet with tiny diamonds on the edge of each green blade.

It suddenly popped into her mind that she was not alone. Where had those dirty brown shoes come from? And those raggedy-looking denim legs didn't look at all like Daddy's. Who dared to walk in her orchard? With a quick flip of her body and a little scrambling, she was soon on a branch three feet higher than the man could reach without some climbing.

"What are you doing in my orchard?" She gazed down at a man with an ugly scar across one side of his face.

The eyes that stared back at her were a deep, bright blue. He was holding a lighted cigarette in one hand. "You're some little monkey, young lady. Does your mother know you're out here?"

"Mama knows I'm just about always in the orchard if I'm not in the house. Why aren't you at your own house?"

He sighed heavily. "I can't stay at my house anymore." He threw the cigarette into the grass and stepped on it. "People don't want me around anymore, so I have to find some place to stay."

"You don't live in this town, I guess."

He sighed again. "No, I don't. But I need a place to sleep for a while, and then I can go on. Places are hard to find."

"Then you should ask Jesus for a place to sleep, 'cause He knows where to find everything. How come you're looking so funny at me?"

"Because I don't know your Jesus and I don't know how to talk to Him."

"Well," Kyla began, taking a step down, "you just talk to Him as you do to anybody, only you have to be very polite 'cause He's the most important person in the world."

The man shook his head. "Maybe He won't listen to me after what I've done."

Kyla took another step down to the next branch. "Oh, yes, He will! He'll listen to you, 'cause He's always listening for people who need help, 'specially if they don't know Him. If you shut your eyes and bow your head, I'll talk to Him. Uh—what's your name?"

"Pete. Peter Halversen. OK?"

"OK. Dear Jesus, this is uh—Peter Hal-ver-sen. I know You know who he is, 'cause You can see him standing under my cherry tree. He needs a place to sleep, Jesus, where nobody can find him for a while, so if it's all right with You, someplace where there's hay or some—oh, thank You, Jesus! That's a good idea, and watch over him and help him to be a good boy—I mean, man—and make things come out all right for him. Amen."

"Thank you, young lady." The man had to clear his

throat a couple of times before he could say more. "You must be pretty well acquainted with Jesus."

"He's my very best friend." She scrambled down the tree and started through the long orchard grasses. "Jesus said you could use our hayloft, and there's an old blanket up there we use for sliding sometimes. But you mustn't smoke, 'cause they would smell it, and my daddy doesn't smoke cigarettes."

"I wish I didn't either."

Kyla turned her big brown eyes up at him. "You can ask Jesus to help you stop. Now, just lock the door when you go up, and I won't let anyone play up there today. I'll pick some apples for you and make you a sandwich and put it in the car part of the barn after Daddy goes to work."

"Thank you very much, young lady. Now I think you'd better go back to bed. It's only 22 minutes after 4:00. I'm sure your parents won't like it if they find you out here at this hour talking to a strange man. Good night."

Slipping quietly into the house, Kyla went upstairs and back to bed.

Later that day the neighbor children and Rhoda couldn't get Kyla interested in playing in the hayloft, and they grudgingly consented to play in the front yard between the five plum trees on the east and the five cherry trees on the west. Soon they heard a voice call "Suppertime!"

When Kyla's family was seated around the oak table

and Mr. Jemron had asked the blessing on their food, a shadow darkened the screen door and a knock sounded.

"Oh!" exclaimed Kyla. "That's my friend."

"Well, if you know him, maybe you should invite him in," suggested Mr. Jemron. "He might be hungry."

Kyla ran to the door. "Hi, Mr. Halversen. Are you hungry? My daddy said to invite you in."

Mr. Halversen seemed nervous and hesitated, but when Kyla ran for an extra chair and Rhoda put a plate, glass, and silverware on the table, he sat down beside the little girl he had met in the orchard in the late hours of the night. "I—I shouldn't, but I'm hungry, really hungry. All I've had in the past three days was a few apples and the two sandwiches your little daughter put in the garage part of the barn for me. I don't know whether she said anything, but I've been there since early this morning—sleeping most of the time."

Rhoda exclaimed, "So that's why you wouldn't let us play in the hayloft today!"

"He needed to sleep" was all Kyla said, and she continued eating as if such things were a daily happening.

"Sir, I am 33 years old, and never has anyone talked to me about Jesus or prayed with me as your little girl did last night. I thank you for your food, and now I have a request to make."

"Ask," replied Mr. Jemron.

"I want you to call the sheriff and tell him that Peter Halversen is sitting at your table and that I will be here when he arrives. Because of your little girl's prayers, I'm going to be a better man. Because of her faith in Jesus, I've found a new Friend also."

After he had gone off with a mighty surprised sheriff, the family went back into the house, where Mr. Jemron just stared in amazement at his daughter. He shook his head. "It will be a long time before you really understand the full impact of what has happened. I can hardly believe it myself. Just remember this—don't ever again get up and go outdoors by yourself in the middle of the night."

"Why, Daddy? I thought it was daytime—it looked like it almost. Why did they take him away, and what did the sheriff mean when he said Mr. Halversen was 'wanted'?"

"Sit down, Kyla." Her father's hands were trembling. "If I had known he was out there, I would have been afraid myself to have gone outside. Do you usually wake up in the middle of the night?"

"No, Daddy."

He sighed. "Well, let's say God woke you to do a job that older people would be afraid to do. When you get to heaven—and if Mr. Halversen doesn't change his mind about following Jesus—you will have at least one star in your crown."

"But, Daddy . . ."

He shook his head. "I'll tell you this and no more: Your new friend, who has accepted Jesus, has to spend the rest of his life in prison for murder. We won't discuss any more of it. Just be thankful Jesus walked by your side this morning."

Kyla heaved a big sigh. "I knew Jesus could help him. He can help anybody who will let Him."

10

Testimony to Caroline

by Enola Fargusson

Because we don't know her name, we'll call her Caroline.* She was a Seventh-day Adventist girl who lived in California about 100 years ago.

Caroline's parents were poor in goods but rich in God's love. "He takes care of us in so many ways," they would say at evening worship, recounting the day's blessings.

That expression—"in so many ways"—bothered Caroline. It wasn't that she didn't believe in God. She just didn't think He was interested in every little thing—or in unimportant people.

"He has a whole universe to run," she would say. "He can't be bothered with us."

More than anything in the world, Caroline wanted to get a college education. And college took money, even back then. So every evening, when her chores were fin-

---

*Some minor details and dialogue have also been supplied.

ished, she tutored some of her slower classmates, putting every penny she earned into a special fund.

To go to an Adventist college, Caroline would have to travel all the way to Michigan. But one day she heard some good news. The church was going to build a college in northern California. The small town of Healdsburg was selected as the site, and in April 1882 the school opened.

Caroline did all the work she could find, but her small hoard of coins for college grew much too slowly. Finally, in desperation, she wrote the college officials, explaining her plight. Back came an answer that delighted her. She could teach some classes to help pay her expenses. And Ellen White, widowed and living near the college, was opening her home to some of the girl students. Caroline could stay there.

"It's an answer to prayer," her parents declared.

And their daughter smiled at their "innocence."

Healdsburg College was smaller than most of our academies today. There were only two buildings, and they were three blocks apart. The school building had 10 rooms for offices and classrooms. The boardinghouse had a dining room, parlor, and president's quarters on the first floor, girls' rooms on the second, and boys' rooms on the third. The kitchen and laundry were in the basement.

Mrs. White lived in a farmhouse that was comfortable but not lavish. Living quarters occupied the main floor, while the bedrooms were on the smaller second story.

The school program was a busy one—classes in the

mornings, work in the afternoons, and study in the evenings. Dorm lights went out at 9:30 p.m.

In accordance with the health principles that had been revealed to Mrs. White, two meals a day were served both in her home and at the school, with breakfast at 7:00 a.m. and dinner at 2:00 p.m. Fruit was allowed in the evening, if necessary, but there were no junk foods around.

The first few weeks were exciting for Caroline. She and the other girls quickly grew to love Mrs. White, who treated them all like daughters. Caroline especially liked evening worship, when Mrs. White would gather the girls before the living room fireplace and tell them stories from her own experience.

Life would have been perfect for Caroline if she had only had a little spending money. She didn't need much, but she wished she had a few cents to buy herself something once in a while. All her money went directly to the school.

The girls dressed simply and without frills. Mrs. White had assigned Caroline and her roommate, Lucy, a small room with a comfortable bed, a study table, and a kerosene lamp. They each had brought a trunk in which they kept their personal belongings.

One afternoon, in the busy time between classes and dinner, Caroline needed something. Perhaps it was a pair of scissors or some pins. Whatever it was, she stepped into Mrs. White's bedroom to borrow it as she had been given permission to do.

Except for the girls preparing dinner in the kitchen downstairs, she was alone in the house. So when she saw a silk hairnet on Mrs. White's dresser, she couldn't resist trying it on.

"How pretty!" she said aloud, turning her head to admire her hair in the mirror. She stood there for several minutes. Suddenly she heard the front door slam.

She snatched the net off her hair, and hurrying across the hall to her own bedroom, she slipped it into the top tray of her trunk. *After all,* she thought, *Mrs. White probably has a drawer full of hairnets. She won't miss it.*

But Caroline was wrong. Mrs. White did miss it. That very afternoon she was going to put it on before going out and couldn't find it. She searched high and low, even moving the dresser away from the wall.

Finally she gave up, but her heart was heavy. There could be only one explanation. One of the girls must have taken it.

That evening, when the girls gathered around the fireplace for worship, Mrs. White looked solemn. "Has anyone seen my silk hairnet?" she asked.

"Is it missing?" Caroline inquired.

"I'm afraid so," Mrs. White replied. "I put it on my dresser this morning, but when I went to get it this afternoon, it was gone."

The other girls sat in stunned silence.

Finally Mrs. White suggested, "Shall we pray about it?"

As Caroline knelt with her friends, she felt strange. What if someone saw it in her trunk? Would she be banished in disgrace?

The girl hardly slept that night. She knew now that she could never wear the hairnet. And not just for fear of discovery. She had betrayed a true friend. She wished she had never seen the net.

A few days later Mrs. White mentioned it again during evening worship. "Do any of you have anything to tell me about my hairnet?" she asked. "I'm sure someone here knows where it is. It couldn't have walked away by itself."

Caroline squirmed inwardly, hoping her discomfort didn't show on her face.

That night in bed she whispered to Lucy, "Why is Mrs. White making such a fuss over her hairnet? She has plenty of money. Why doesn't she just buy another?"

Lucy whispered back, "Some of the royalties on her books she turns right back to the church. And by the time she gets through helping others with what's left, she doesn't have that much to spend on herself. Just think what it's costing her to feed the lot of us, even with her garden and orchard."

Caroline's face flamed with embarrassment. Mrs. White had been good to her—like a second mother. It was a real privilege to live in her house. She loved to listen to the stories Mrs. White told and to read the messages that God had sent through her to ministers and church leaders.

Her embarrassment turned to chagrin. *I've never taken anything before*, she thought. *How could I have been so stupid? If I'm caught, I'll be sent home. I'll never be able to attend another college. It would be the end of all my dreams.*

The next morning, as soon as Lucy left their room, Caroline got rid of the hairnet in a way she thought no one would ever know.

The next few days went by smoothly. Caroline pushed the incident to the back of her mind, and Mrs. White seemed to have forgotten about it also.

Then one day she asked Caroline to step into her room.

"I have something to tell you," Mrs. White said quietly. She closed her door and invited Caroline to sit down.

"It's about my hairnet," Mrs. White began. "Shortly after it disappeared, I was walking past your room when my eyes fell on your trunk. A voice said to me, 'Open the trunk.' Of course I didn't want to. It didn't belong to me. But I heard the voice again, saying, 'Lift the lid off that trunk.' This time I recognized it as the voice of an angel. So I obeyed, and there in your top tray was my missing hairnet. That's why I mentioned the matter a second time during worship. I wanted you to tell me you had taken it."

Caroline's eyes filled with tears. "You've known all along?" she asked. "Oh, I wish I'd never seen it. How ungrateful you must think I am, after all you've done for me."

"Later I was sitting by the fireplace writing," Mrs.

White continued. "I had been working for quite a while and my hand was tired from holding the pen, so I leaned back to rest. Suddenly I had a very short vision. I saw a girl's hand holding my hairnet over the flame of a kerosene lamp. There was a flash of light, and the silk net was gone."

Caroline began to tremble. "God sent you a vision about me?" she asked. "But I'm not important. I'm nobody."

"Oh, my dear," Mrs. White exclaimed, "God gave His Son for you. Do you value His gift so little? Do you believe He made such a sacrifice for nobody?"

Suddenly it seemed to Caroline as if a fog lifted. "I've always loved God," she said, "but I never believed until now that He cared about little things."

"We humans divide things into little and big, important and unimportant," Mrs. White said. "With God there is no difference. Sin is sin. Human beings are His children. He cares about everything."

"Can you forgive me for stealing and destroying your hairnet?" Caroline asked, tears streaming down her cheeks.

"Of course I forgive you, as God will," Mrs. White said. "I think you have learned a valuable lesson."

Caroline gave her heart to God that very minute, and from then on she never doubted His loving concern. She knew He cares about little things.

11

Beware—Dangerous Bull

by Enid Sparks

It seemed to Del that the afternoon was dragging on and on. He'd taken a walk around the farm. He'd tried reading a book, but he was in the mood for some action.

How I wish Jim were home! he thought. *Then we could have some fun.*

Jim was Del's best friend. He lived on the farm across the road and was always good for a game of basketball or a hike in the woods. But he had gone away for the weekend.

Del's mother noticed his unrest. "Why don't you try the new game Uncle Bob brought yesterday?" she suggested, putting down her sewing. "I'll get it for you."

"No thanks, Mom." Del jammed his hands into his pockets. "I think I'll go over to Harry's house."

Del's mother straightened in her chair and gathered up her sewing. Her actions spoke louder than any words she could have uttered. Del knew she didn't approve of his hanging around with Harry Davis and the group of older boys who were always visiting the Davis dairy farm.

Harry's gang had some bad habits. They played "chicken" while riding bicycles, smoked cigarettes, and thought up pranks to pull on one another. It was these pranks that fascinated Del. "They're always doing such exciting things, Mom," he'd remarked several times.

Del's mother had never forbidden him to see the boys. But she had said, "A lot of the things Harry and his friends do aren't Christian in nature, son. Perhaps you should pray about your association with them."

But Del hadn't prayed. Somehow he didn't think it necessary to bother God with anything so unimportant as whom to spend time with. *After all, it isn't as if they're good friends*, he thought. *It's just that they're fun to do things with sometimes*.

As Del opened the front door to go out, Mother cautioned, "Please take care, son."

"OK, Mom," he answered, just as he always did. Ever since his father had been killed in an automobile accident last year, Mother was constantly warning him to be careful.

Walking down the wide country road perked up Del's spirits. Soon he was whistling a lively little song he had heard Harry sing. He was still whistling it as he strolled under the aluminum arch that read "Davis Dairy" and up the tree-lined drive. He was almost at the house when he heard Harry calling from one of the corrals.

"Down here, Del! Come and get a look at this beauty!"

Del wondered what Harry could be talking about as he followed the path toward the barns. Probably a new type of milking machine.

But it wasn't a milker that Harry and the other boys were admiring. It was a huge purebred Holstein bull.

"Isn't he incredible?" Harry asked in awe. "Dad just brought him home yesterday."

Del knew very little about dairy cattle, but the animal standing in the middle of the corral did seem magnificent. His black-and-white hide reflected the sunlight and looked like shimmering satin stretched over his brawny muscles.

Del whispered appreciatively, "He's a big one."

"Yeah, and a wild one, too!" exclaimed John, one of Harry's friends. "He pawed up a storm a little while ago. You should've seen the dust fly!"

Del gulped. "Then—then shouldn't we move back from the fence? He might charge right through it."

Harry scoffed at the idea. "Naw, this fence is stouter than any old bull! Dad had a bigger, meaner one than him in here last year."

Del had just caught sight of a red-and-white sign swinging high above the gate. "But the sign . . ." he stammered. "It says, 'Beware—Dangerous Bull.'"

Del was getting ready to retreat when Harry said, "Oh, don't worry so much. Come on over here and climb up on the railing so you can see the full size of this critter. Man, he's really something!"

Del wanted to say that he could see that the bull was "something" without climbing up, but he didn't want the others to think he was afraid. When Harry swung up to the top railing, Del climbed up beside him.

"OK, wave the cape!" Harry shouted, grinning back over his shoulder at John. "Let's show Del some real action."

Del had time only to glance backward and see John swinging a large red bandanna before he heard an angry bellow close at hand. Terror-stricken, he whirled about on the railing. The enraged bull was charging straight at him and Harry.

"Jump down!" shouted Harry, dropping from the fence and sprinting away.

But Del froze. Somehow his body wouldn't do what he wanted it to. He could only watch helplessly as the huge animal struck the fence with terrific force. Instantly Del felt himself being hurled through the air and flung to the ground *inside* the corral.

"Get up, Del! Get out of there!" the other boys yelled.

The bull had circled for another charge. Del tried to move, but pain shot up his left leg, paralyzing his whole body.

"Help me!" he cried. "I think my leg is broken!" His words were drowned out by a splintering crash as the bull narrowly missed trampling him and rammed his horns into the fence.

"John, run and get my dad!" ordered Harry. "I'll try

to head the bull off by standing on the fence and jabbing this pitchfork at him."

Lifting his head, Del could see the bull lowering his head to come at him again. He knew a mere pitchfork wouldn't fend off the incensed animal. A thought flashed through his mind—prayer was the only answer.

Closing his eyes, Del whispered the only words he had time to say: "Dear God, please stop the bull!" A few seconds later everything became quiet. Del could no longer hear the bellowing bull or the shouting boys.

Opening his eyes, he looked around. The first thing he saw was the bull trotting away toward the opposite end of the corral. Harry, openmouthed and deathly pale, stood beside Del, shaking his head.

"I can't believe it!" the bewildered boy gasped. "Whatever made that beast turn away like that?"

"It was prayer," Del answered softly. "I knew you couldn't stop him with just a pitchfork, so I asked God to protect me."

A strange expression crossed Harry's face. But before Del could figure out what it meant, a black blanket of pain engulfed him, blotting everything into nothingness.

Hours later Del awoke in a hospital bed and saw Mother sitting beside him. At the sight of her worried face, he remembered all her warnings. "Oh, Mom, you were right!" he burst out. "I'm sorry I didn't stay away from Harry and his friends. Now you'll have a big hospital bill to pay, and you won't have me to help you run the farm and do the chores."

Gently Del's mother patted his hand and smiled as she comforted him. "The Lord worked everything out for the best, son. Your hospital bill will be a small price to pay for the miracle that happened today!"

Del's surprise was evident. "Miracle! What miracle?"

"The one God worked for Harry," Mother answered, her eyes shining. "He believes in God now. He told me on the way to the hospital that when he saw how your prayers stopped the bull, he couldn't help believing. And to make up for your being hurt, he and his friends are going to help me on the farm till you're well again."

Del couldn't control the tightness that grew in his throat. "Oh, Mom," he murmured, "that's wonderful. With results like that, I don't even mind having a broken leg!"

12

Beautiful? Who, Me?

by Veryl I. Rogers

Beth Ann stood in front of the cracked mirror in her room. As she glanced down at the old skirt and sweater she wore, anger rose in her throat. It was bad enough to be pudgy and freckled, but to have to wear old hand-me-down rags added insult to injury.

What the other kids say is true, she thought. *I am ugly and dumpy. Maybe if I had better clothes, the kids would like me*.

"Beth Ann, hurry up. Your breakfast is ready," her mom called from the kitchen.

Beth Ann hurried down the stairs. "Mornin', sweetie," Mom said as she set a bowl of cereal in front of her. "It's going to be a lovely day."

"All things bright and beautiful . . . the Lord God made them all" floated softly through Beth Ann's mind. She watched her mom hurrying around the shabby but spotless kitchen. Mom was clever with her hands and performed miracles with next to nothing.

"Mom, do you ever wish we had lots of money?" Beth Ann said as she dipped her spoon into the cereal bowl.

"Honey, I've never really given that much thought." Mom checked the stove. "We've always been so fortunate that I'd feel ashamed even suggesting to the good Lord that He'd neglected our family."

Beth Ann closed her eyes. How could she tell Mom that she needed a new dress because she'd been chosen to sing at the school concert? So far she'd kept it a secret because she wasn't sure she would actually sing. The shock of what she'd overheard yesterday still haunted her.

At first the excitement had been more than she could stand when Mrs. Dyer, the music teacher, had announced that Beth Ann would sing the opening solo for the concert. It wasn't until afternoon that she had overheard the three girls talking about her.

"I am so sick and tired of hearing Beth Ann sing, sing, sing all the time," Kara sneered. "Every time we have an assembly she gets to sing."

"Yes, and to see her standing up on that stage in those dumpy dresses makes me sick!" Jessica gave a shrill, ugly laugh.

"Plus she's a big tub of lard," Amy snickered.

"I think I'll have my mom complain to the principal about this whole thing!" exclaimed Kara. Tossing her blond curls, she stomped down the hall. Her two friends hurried along behind her.

Beth Ann had stood transfixed with horror. Fear, hurt, and shame engulfed her. She had never thought much about how she sounded—much less how she looked—when she sang. Pastor Robins had said people should use the talents God gave them, and she assumed singing was her talent. But how could she stand up there and sing after this?

Now as Beth Ann sat at the breakfast table, her mind flew in circles. How could she ever approach her mother about the dress?

"Hi, everybody!" 10-year-old Mike shouted as he came hurtling into the kitchen. He reached for the milk and poured it over his cereal with a splash. "Hey, Mom, isn't it great? Sis has been asked to sing the opening solo at the concert that's coming up."

With a gasp of surprise Beth Ann glanced at her mother. Leave it to Mike!

Mom turned, face aglow, and exclaimed with pride, "Beth Ann! Why didn't you tell me?"

"Oh, Mom, I'm sorry, but I haven't made up my mind whether I'll do it or not." Busily she gathered the dishes and placed them in the sink.

"What do you mean, you haven't made up your mind? Why, dear, it's such an honor to be asked to sing. You'd actually turn it down?"

"I'll think about it, OK?" Beth Ann gave her mother a hug as she gathered up her books. "I'll be home right after school and help with the ironing."

"All right," Mom said as she watched her daughter

hurry down the sidewalk. What could be the matter? Many times during the day Mom stopped her work to say a silent prayer for Beth Ann and the problem that seemed to be burdening her.

All morning a sick feeling lay in the pit of Beth Ann's stomach. Each time she glanced at Kara the hurt grew bigger. The sound of the girls' voices giggling the day before echoed in her mind.

Closing her eyes as she bent over her paper, she sent a short prayer to God. *Please, God, help me not to care what they say. Help me forgive them. And most of all . . . I guess . . . help me just to be glad I'm me.*

The lunch bell rang, and the room emptied with a scurry of papers, pencils, and books. Beth Ann slowly gathered her things, agonizing over whether to eat lunch in the cafeteria or outside, where she wouldn't have to listen to the whispers and snickers around her.

"Beth Ann, would you stay a moment? I'd like to talk with you before you leave," Miss Martin said with a smile. Miss Martin was her homeroom teacher and a favorite of all the students.

Beth Ann looked at her questioningly. In the instant that their eyes met she knew Miss Martin had heard what the girls had said.

"Beth Ann, I have something for you, and I hope you will accept it with as much joy as I find in giving it. I've wanted to do this for a long time but didn't know how to go about it. When I heard that you had been chosen to sing for the concert, I decided that now was the appropriate time." She handed Beth Ann a large, brightly wrapped box.

Hands trembling, Beth Ann opened the box, and there lying in the soft tissue paper was one of the most beautiful dresses she'd ever seen. The soft pink of the gossamer folds shimmered in the sunlight.

Glancing up with stunned surprise, she was about to speak when Miss Martin raised her hand and shushed her, saying, "Just be happy, Beth Ann, and never take away from others the joy of giving."

"It's so beautiful! I don't know what to say," Beth Ann sighed. "But, well, I may not sing after all." Slowly tears filled her eyes, and she wiped them away with her sleeve.

"What do you mean?" Miss Martin asked.

"Well . . . I just . . . am not sure whether . . . I want to." Beth Ann looked out the window.

"Beth Ann, I think I know what the problem is, but running away from problems will never solve them. And believe me, they have to be solved somehow." Her hands neatly stacked the papers on her desk, giving Beth Ann time to think.

"You have a lovely voice. It's God's gift to you. Never, never allow others to govern the good you can do by the things they say and do. But most of all, remember that you are God's creation. How could you ever be anything but beautiful?" The older woman placed the box in Beth Ann's arms and led her to the door.

"I'm looking forward to hearing you sing, and when I see you standing there in that beautiful dress, I'll be happy for you. But remember, the dress isn't the important thing. It's the person inside that counts." Smiling, Miss Martin gently closed the door behind her.

Beth Ann stood there for a moment, clutching the box with shaking hands. The sad, cold feeling in the pit of her stomach was gone. In its place was the calm assurance that she really was OK.

Suddenly it dawned on her that she hadn't even said thank you. Quickly she turned to open the door. Through its glass window she saw Miss Martin's head bowed over clasped hands, and somehow she knew the teacher's prayer was especially for her.

And the reminder that God had made her and she was beautiful in His eyes had changed her life. Quietly she tiptoed down the hall, the words "All things bright and beautiful" singing in her heart.

13

Caught in Quicksand

by Mary Weiss Futcher

When I was 15 I got hired as a junior counselor at a YWCA camp on the shores of Lake Geneva, Wisconsin. It was called Camp Eleanor. Even the name delighted me.

I'd lived in Chicago all my life—not a bad place, but obviously crowded. My family was Jewish, and while I halfheartedly professed my heritage, I had no real belief in a personal God. Such thoughts were far from my mind, though, as I left the city looking forward to a glorious summer.

The high point of each camp session was a hike around the lake—some 35 miles. We called this Hitchhike Day, for arrangements had been made with people running commercial boats on the lake to pick up tired hikers and return them to camp for a small fee.

As soon as I heard about Hitchhike Day, I knew I just had to make the hike. But the first five weeks of camp found me assigned to helping with swimming or archery while most of the group went hiking.

At last my time came—I was asked to lead six girls around the lake. It thrilled me that I was given the responsibility and the chance to complete the 35-mile hike. I had no doubt that I could do it, and the fact that no one else had completed it that summer made me even more determined to be the first.

The head director gave me a map that plainly showed the route we were to take. As I looked over the map, I noticed an area of quicksand. It was nothing to worry about, of course—just something to stay away from. I made a mental picture of the map and then folded it and put it in my pocket.

My six girls were as eager to begin as I was, so we took off early. We skirted the edge of beautiful Lake Eleanor all morning. By noon we all felt glad to stop and eat our sack lunches and dangle our feet in the cool water. Three of the girls decided to go back, so they flagged down one of the boats. But four of us kept on going. As we walked, we laughed and giggled over silly things, paying no attention to the map, which was all but forgotten in my pocket.

After we'd hiked several more miles and enjoyed looking at the mansions built on the lakeshore, we came to a narrow path. Should we take it? Why not! It seemed to be going in the right direction. We had to walk single file, as the trail became narrow and steep. I walked several yards ahead of the girls, just enjoying looking at the summer birds. Then suddenly I stepped into what I thought was water.

I yelped as my feet got wet. I decided to back up, but my feet wouldn't move. As I began to sink, I realized that I'd stumbled into quicksand. I felt as though something had hold of my legs and was pulling me down. It was the strangest sensation I'd ever experienced. I wasn't scared at first, but I yelled to the girls behind me to stop where they were and send someone for help.

One of them remembered that we'd seen a farmer plowing a field with two workhorses a mile or so back, so one of the girls raced off in that direction. The others stood by helpless, and I began to grow panicky.

One of the girls yelled to me to put my arms over my head. Time passed, and slowly, relentlessly, my body sank into the ground. I was totally unable to stop it. My arms grew heavy and tired. My body felt as though it were being squeezed into a ball.

Finally in the distance I could hear the *clap, clap* of horses' hooves, but it seemed so far away. I felt as though I'd been there for hours; I was nearly up to my chest in that dragging, pulling, tightening hole.

Feeling my body being sucked down into death, I sensed that Satan had me all in his power. And then suddenly my thoughts shifted to God in heaven, and I wondered if He would hear the voice of one who rarely prayed.

Without a word, but in the depths of my mind, I

called out to God. Even then I wondered if He'd listen. My prayers before had been silly, foolish things, offered only at times when I'd wanted to satisfy some whim. I didn't know God. But I called out to Him as my shoulders sank beneath the sand.

Was it God's doing that caused the farmer to arrive just as my chin was sinking into the mire and my head was tilted upward, my eyes turned wistfully toward heaven—or was it just a lucky chance? Anyway, the farmer tossed a rope over my head and managed to get it under my armpits. My arms were limp with exhaustion, and I hardly knew what was happening.

I lost consciousness as the farmer attached the rope to the strong horses and directed them to pull. They heaved and tugged until they pulled me from my prison of death.

Someone took me to the nearest hospital, where I was cleaned up and my scratches and bruises were cared for. I stayed for observation and then returned to camp a few days later.

I'd had time to think of my narrow escape as I lay in the hospital bed. What if the farmer hadn't been there? What if we hadn't seen him plowing? The girls would never have known where to go for help. What if he had been a few minutes longer in coming?

In the last moments before my certain death, was it God Himself who'd directed my thoughts to Him?

Why did I stumble into the quicksand in the first place? I'd had a map. The map showed the quicksand.

But I hadn't followed it. I realized with a sudden start that maps have a purpose—to guide us. Could the Bible be a map to guide people on the road of life? Should I study the book that many people called God's book—the Bible?

That was the beginning of my search for truth, the search that led me to Christ.

14

Roscoe to the Rescue

by Nina Coombs Pykare

You might have thought I'd ask God for help with a problem like this. But I didn't think I had a problem. So it never occurred to me to bring God into it. I thought the fault was all Mom's—and Peter's.

I didn't like Peter. He was tall and skinny with a bald spot on the back of his head. He had a goofy laugh, sort of horselike. And he smiled funny, too. But mostly I didn't like him because he'd married Mom.

Mom met Peter at church. She said that he was a good man, that his wife was dead and he didn't have any children. And in truth, he was always polite to me. It was just—well, a girl's only got one father.

Mom and Peter and I went to Disney World on "our" honeymoon. Yes, they took me along. Peter was always doing nice things for me. But I figured the trip was really Mom's idea.

I especially wanted to go on the Space Mountain roller coaster. Maybe I got my love of high places from my dad. "Up there on the high iron," he had said, "you can tell a man from a mouse."

When I saw Space Mountain, I forgot everything else. "Come on!" I cried. "Let's go!"

Peter took one look at the towering ride. He laughed that goofy laugh. "Not me. Three feet up, and I freeze."

I had a sudden picture of Dad walking across the open steel girders of a new building so many stories above the ground, acting as cool as if he were in his own backyard.

I sighed. Peter was a wimp, too.

Things became even worse when we got home. Peter had this attitude about cats.

Now, I'll admit that Roscoe's not the best-behaved cat in the world. He has long white hair that sticks to everything, and he never comes when he's called unless he's hungry. And he has this really dumb habit of running away every chance he gets.

But he's mine; he's part of the family.

"Cats are good-for-nothing animals," Peter began to complain. He'd say the same thing every time he had to pick white hairs off his dark suit. He had some wimpy job in a bank and always went to work wearing a suit.

Of course, I got tired of having white hairs on everything too. But I would never have told Peter that.

I could see Mom was worried about us. Oh, I wasn't

mean to Peter. I just didn't talk to him unless I had to. After all, Mom hadn't asked about my feelings when she'd gotten the divorce. Oh, she talked to me—a lot of stuff about how she and Dad both still loved me, about how they each just wanted different things. I didn't notice either one of them asking me what I wanted. But the divorce was done. I had to live with it and with the wimp she'd chosen to marry.

About a month after the honeymoon I came home from school and found Roscoe missing. He'd pulled some wires out of my bedroom screen and hightailed it out the window. I looked and looked, but I couldn't find him.

I was still looking when Peter came home from work and asked, "What's wrong?"

"Roscoe's gone. He ripped open the screen and took off."

"Any idea where he'd go?"

I shook my head. I was trying not to cry. There was a Doberman around the corner that thinks a cat makes a nice dessert. There were all sorts of dogs in our neighborhood, big mean ones.

"I suppose we'd better go out and look for him," Peter said. "You go that way."

I was halfway around the block when I remembered that Peter didn't even like the cat. So what was he doing out looking for him?

After going around the block with nothing to show for it, I turned in our walk. The ladder was leaning against the big maple tree by the side of the house. And on the highest rung stood Peter. I could tell it was Peter by his polished shoes and blue pin-striped pant legs. The rest of him was hidden in the leaves.

Suddenly the ladder started to move! I ran over and grabbed it. "Peter, be careful!" I shouted.

"Here, kitty, kitty." Peter's voice floated down.

I looked up, but all I could see were the soles of his shoes and his wrinkled blue socks, covered with white cat hairs.

Peter's shoes moved just a little. "I've got him. Keep the ladder steady."

It took a long while for Peter to back down the ladder. Finally he stood on the ground. His face was so pale it scared me. Sweat was running down into his white shirt. He stood for a minute, taking some deep breaths. Then he reached inside his coat and handed me a trembling Roscoe.

"You silly cat," I scolded, yet hugged him close. "You could have been killed."

I turned to Peter. He made a motion with his hand and took off behind the garage. I heard him being sick there. It didn't seem like the right time for saying thank you. I took Roscoe into the house and locked him in my room, making sure the window was shut tight.

When I started back through the kitchen, Peter was just coming in. He sat down at the table as if he couldn't stand up for another minute.

"How about a glass of water?" I asked. I was beginning to feel real stupid about the way I'd been treating him. I mean, my own father never helped me look for the cat.

He nodded. "Sounds good."

I filled a glass and put it in front of him. Then I took his coat off the back of the chair and started picking cat hairs off it. "Why'd you do a thing like that?" I asked. "Why'd you climb up that ladder?"

He laughed his goofy laugh. It sounded different somehow. Nicer. "I was afraid she'd get away before you got back."

Now that I was really paying attention to him, Peter wasn't so wimpy-looking. "But you're scared of high places," I reminded him.

"You'd better believe it. I fell out of a tree when I was a kid. Spent a long time in the hospital."

"Then why'd you go up the ladder?"

He frowned and rubbed his bald spot. "It seemed like the right thing to do. You love Roscoe, and I care about you. So I'm bound to care about the cat, too."

He smiled that funny smile. It seemed different, too. I sort of liked it.

"I know you don't like me much," he went on. "I'm not at all like your father. I'm not strong and handsome. I don't lead a life of adventure. But I take care of my family. I might get scared, but I do what needs to be done."

I got up and went to the junk drawer for the roll of masking tape. "Look, Peter," I said, "the cat really is a lot of trouble. Sometimes I am too." I took a deep breath. "But things are going to be different now."

He watched while I tore off a strip of tape. "The first thing I'm going to do is show you how to get the cat hairs off your clothes." I wrapped the tape around my hand, sticky side out, ready for action.

Following my lead, Peter reached for the tape and tore off a piece. But he didn't realize we were both headed for the same area of his suit. Our hands landed on top of each other.

"Looks like we're sorta sticking together," Peter observed.

I couldn't have said it better.

15

Sally and the Amazing Leaping Crocodiles

by Sally Dillon

"Let's go make faces at the monkeys," my sister, Janice, shouted as she ran ahead across the footbridge.

My mom and baby sister followed her, but I hung back, staring in fascination at the lazy crocodiles beneath me. They lay in the bottom of their pond, unmoving. I wondered if the officials at this zoo in Ghana had put rubber reptiles in the pond to save on upkeep expenses. *Why aren't the crocs moving?* I wondered.

As I continued peering at the seemingly lifeless crocodiles, a guy walked past me and kicked some gravel off the bridge onto the sleeping giants.

Suddenly the beasts sprang to life, jaws snapping, tails thrashing! It was magnificent! Sort of like the prince waking the sleeping beauty, except that with their rugged, scaly skin and jagged, toothy underbites, these crocs weren't exactly beautiful.

"Sally, are you coming?" called Mom.

"In a second," I answered, not moving from my spot on the bridge.

Soon the crocodiles had resumed their rubber poses, and the water slowly rippled back to a calm state.

A thought struck me. If the gravel trick worked for that guy, it should work for me. With a sly smile I pushed some gravel off the bridge with the toe of my flip-flops.

With a crash, the peaceful water erupted in spray as the crocs' huge jaws snapped. It was incredible. Then back to the bottom of the pond they sank, rippling water the only sign of the drama just moments before.

Dad and Mom had always taught me to be kind to animals, but surely those rules couldn't apply to these big ugly dudes. They were reptiles and were supposedly mean. Anyway, as long as they didn't catch me, who would know? And what difference did it make, anyway . . . right?

I glanced up to see how far Mom and my little sisters had gone. They were over talking to the ostriches. Mom was hidden by the wall of the ostrich enclosure, and I couldn't see her, which meant she couldn't see me.

I imagined the voice of the circus ringmaster shouting over the loudspeakers: "And now, ladies and gentlemen, give a round of applause to Sally and her amazing leaping crocodiles!" The crowd went wild! With a quick flick of my ankle I kicked more gravel onto the crocodiles. As they leaped out of the water in fury the imaginary applause was deafening!

Strangely, the angry reptiles did not go back to snoozing on the bottom of their pool. Instead, they cruised around menacingly, their cold eyes seeming to fixate on me above them. I blinked, thankful for the iron bars holding up the railing I was leaning over. Still, the bridge felt awfully low and close to the water.

The adrenaline pumped through my body with each beat of my heart, making me tingle with excitement. I felt as though I could do anything, outrun, outjump, outsmart any beast of jungle. After all, I was Sally the Magnificent!

Scraping together an even bigger pile of gravel, I waited for the right moment when the biggest croc was directly below me. Ready . . . steady . . . now! I kicked the gravel off with a flourish that made my flip-flop slide forward, causing it to stick out beyond my toes. In the seconds that followed, everything seemed to move in slow motion.

A crocodile snapped its tail downward, and its snout shot out of the water toward me! I lurched backward, shoving my foot out still farther. Its jaws closed over the end of my flip-flop and ripped it from me, jamming my foot under the railing, with my bleeding toes sticking over the edge of the bridge. I jerked my trapped foot back and sat shaking in the middle of the bridge as far from each side as I could possibly get. I held my injured foot close, counting my toes. Thankfully, they were all still there. The blood seemed to be coming from a couple of places where my flip-flop straps had scraped the skin off as the shoe had been torn from me. There was another bruise and scrape on the top of my foot, the result of being jammed under the bridge railing.

"Sally!" called my mom. "Come on and stay with us. Don't keep hanging out by yourself. Stay with the group, or I won't bring you back here again!"

Staying close to my mom sounded pretty good right now. "Coming!" I called back.

Wobbling to my feet, I tried to calm my churning stomach. The pool of reptiles was calm and quiet, but the biggest one held my flip-flop triumphantly in its jaws.

I caught up with my family.

"Oh, honey, did your other flip-flop break?" asked Mom sympathetically. Then she spotted my wounds. "Sally! What on earth happened to you?"

"Well, I was sort of pretending that the crocodiles were part of my circus and . . ." I went on to explain the situation. I may make more than my share of mistakes, but at least I'm honest about them.

As the color returned to Mom's skin she corralled us toward the exit. "We've got to get some antiseptic on those scrapes, Sally. I'm sorry our day had to end like this."

My sister Janice glared at me for being the one responsible for bringing the zoo trip to an end. But seeing wild animals had pretty much lost its appeal for me.

As I reflected on my adventure from the back seat of the car, I decided that maybe the rule about kindness to animals was a good one after all and that I should probably apply the rule to all of God's creatures—even reptiles. And I guess coming when Mom calls isn't a half-bad idea either. Yup, those leaping crocodiles taught me a thing or two that I'd never forget.

Meanwhile, back at the zoo, shreds of rubber flip-flop floated on the sun-dappled water . . .

16

Saved by a Song

by Rich Edison

Silently the Confederate sniper hid behind a tree near the small stream bordering the Union encampment. Since dusk he'd been stealthily working his way toward this spot. The skills he'd learned as a teenager hunting deer back home had proved valuable in helping him escape detection. A couple of times he'd accidentally stepped on a dry branch, and the resulting crack seemed like a rifle shot in the stillness of the dark forest. Instantly he'd frozen in place, his ears straining for any sound that might indicate he'd been heard. But he hadn't seen any Union patrols, and as he checked his rifle he congratulated himself on his skill.

The muted sounds of the Union camp floated to him above the gurgling sounds of the stream. Several soldiers played cards around a campfire. Their raucous laughter and occasional curses disturbed the quiet of the night.

From one tent the rumbling sound of snoring ended abruptly with a loud *whack* as someone apparently threw a boot at the snorer. The sniper suppressed a laugh as he thought of the poor victim trying to figure out in the morning how he'd gotten that bruise.

Suddenly the moon appeared from behind a passing cloud, flooding the camp with light and reminding the sniper why he'd come. His sharp eyes scanned the enemy camp, looking for a likely target. The tents and few soldiers still up at this late hour stood out starkly in the moonlight. Just then, directly across the stream, he saw a sudden movement. A sentry he hadn't noticed before adjusted his heavy rifle to a more comfortable position on his shoulder and leaned back against the giant oak he stood beside. This change in position brought the sentry into the full light of the moon, revealing him clearly to the sniper.

The fool! He'll pay for that mistake, thought the sniper.

Carefully he raised his long rifle into position, centering the enemy soldier in his sights. Silently he pulled the hammer back with his thumb and placed his finger on the trigger. Exhaling slowly, he waited for the rapid pounding of his heart to slow. He couldn't miss at this range. The sentry was as good as dead. *He'll not see the morning*, the sniper thought grimly.

Just as he was about to pull the trigger and send the bullet down the long barrel on its deadly mission, the Union soldier moved. Cursing silently, the sniper repositioned his rifle and once again began to gently squeeze the trigger.

At that moment the sentry raised his eyes toward heaven and in a beautiful baritone voice began to sing. The words came clearly to the ears of the hidden Southerner, and he recognized them as a hymn his mother used to sing: "Saviour, like a shepherd lead us." Relaxing his finger on the trigger, he thought, *I'll just let him finish singing. He's mine anyway. I can't miss.* But as the song's words drifted to his ears, a rush of memories filled the sniper's mind, waking long-forgotten emotions.

A tear furrowed through the dirt on his cheek. He thought of his sweet Christian mother, who had sung him this very song so many times. She had died young, and he still missed her. As the Union soldier finished the last stanza, the sniper found he couldn't aim through his tears, and his hand fell uselessly from the trigger. Slowly he lowered his rifle and turned back toward his own lines. He could not shoot a man who sang like that.

Years passed, the war ended, and the Confederate sniper's and the Union sentry's lives took widely divergent paths. The sniper wandered from place to place, trying to find some meaning and purpose for his life, all the while haunted by the memories of that song heard one moonlit night on a battlefield.

The Union sentry, Ira D. Sankey, became a well-known singing evangelist traveling with the famous preacher Dwight L. Moody. Sankey's melodious voice stirred hearts for Christ around the world. His songbook *Sacred Songs and Solos* became one of the best-selling songbooks of all time. He compiled 10 additional hymnbooks, the profits of which went to support evangelism and to build churches and schools. Sankey composed approximately 80 songs, including "The Ninety and Nine," "Faith Is the Victory," and "Under His Wings." During a series of meetings in London he sang to 2,350,000 people, and many were converted. Everywhere he and Moody went, revival soon followed.

But the paths of the Union sentry turned singing evangelist and the former Confederate sniper were to cross again. On a Christmas Eve in 1875, on a steamboat traveling up the Delaware River, the former sniper heard a voice he remembered from another moonlit night many years before. Making his way to the deck, he saw Ira Sankey leaning against one of the funnels of the boat, just as he had leaned against the oak tree on that far-off battlefield. His eyes again raised toward heaven, Sankey sang the same shepherd song.

Once again the Southerner's sin-hardened heart was stirred. Once again he thought of his childhood and compared it to the rough life he'd led since. But as Sankey's rich baritone voice filled the air, all the pain and despair he'd carried for so long seemed to be lifted away, and the man felt a deep longing to know this Shepherd of which his onetime Civil War enemy sang.

While the last notes of the song still seemed to hang in the chilly air, the former sniper made his way to Sankey's side.

"Sir, do you remember a moonlit night in the early 1860s?" he asked.

"There were many such nights," Sankey replied.

Then tearfully the former sniper told him the story of how he'd nearly ended Sankey's life, and how Sankey had been saved from certain death by the words of the Shepherd's song. He also told of his life since and pleaded with Sankey to help him find the Shepherd of the song.

For a moment Sankey just stood staring openmouthed at the stranger. Then with joy he drew his former enemy close. Moving away from the crowd that had gathered to hear him sing, Sankey gently told this lost sheep about the Good Shepherd. And on that steamboat on Christmas Eve the former sentry and the former sniper knelt together and praised the God who had saved them both.

17

Rescuing Uncle Nat

by Priska Neely

The mouthwatering aroma of peach pie awakened me from my deep sleep. My taste buds were already on the job, and the sweet smells of the Easter meal my mom was cooking beckoned me. Walking into the kitchen, I strolled past the stove and glanced at the digital clock, which seemed especially bright. I was surprised to see that the time was 12:15 a.m.

"Why are you cooking at this time of night?" I sleepily asked my mother.

"Well, tomorrow is Easter Sunday, and I wanted to get an early start on the meal since I thought I'd invite someone home," she muttered between yawns. "Now, you go back to bed."

I sluggishly turned around. As I crawled into bed and snuggled under the covers, my mind filled with thoughts of the Easter Sunday when I was 9 years old.

It had been a cold and breezy Sunday afternoon, and though all of us protested, my mother dragged us to my aunt's church for an Easter service. On our way back from the service I suddenly caught sight of several men huddled around some barrels from which smoke was rising.

"What are those guys doing?" My brother beat me in asking Dad the question.

"Those men are homeless," our father explained. "Since it's so cold outside, they start fires in barrels and huddle around them for warmth."

Just then Mom startled me when she asked, "Aren't these the kind of folks we're supposed to invite home for dinner?"

"No!" my siblings and I yelled in unison.

But to our horror, our parents ignored us. Dad stopped the car. We all stared in disbelief as Dad strolled up to the men. I breathed a sigh of relief as each man my father spoke to shook his head from side to side.

Dad's search was almost complete when a man wearing a T-shirt and holey jeans—and no coat—hobbled up to my father. "I'll come home with you, but I want you to know I'm drunk," the man said. This was already pretty obvious, at least to Dad.

My father pointed to our vehicle. The man headed toward us. Well, sort of. It seemed that in his drunken condition, walking to our car in a straight line was the most challenging task he'd faced in a long time.

Meanwhile we sat silently in the back seat, our minds

racing, wondering what we might say that could convince Dad to leave the man there.

I glanced up at my mother in the front seat. To my surprise, she was smiling! While we were all plotting ways to eliminate this man's presence in our lives, Mom actually seemed happy about bringing him home. What was wrong with her?

She turned to us, her smile still lingering, and said, "Children, if someone comes home with us today, God has already picked that person out."

Why would God pick this guy? I thought. *Surely the Creator of the universe has better taste than to choose him! Maybe this man interfered with God's plans, and if Dad had just gone a little farther down the road, someone else would have accepted the invitation.*

As my dad led him toward the car, I looked at the homeless man's shabby clothing and dirt-covered body. *Well, maybe there is some reason he's coming home with us,* I thought.

My little sister moved to the front seat so the man could sit in the back with us. As soon as Dad opened the door, the man's body odor overwhelmed me. *Maybe if I pretend to faint, Dad will make the man leave,* I reasoned.

"This is Nat," Dad announced and then started the car. I tried not to be rude, but to avoid the smell I turned in the opposite direction and pretended to be in a deep conversation with my brother.

Just then Nat began to laugh. "You're an answer to prayer," he said between chuckles.

"What do you mean?" my dad questioned.

"Well, last night it was so cold that I went and found an abandoned house. There was nothing to lie on, so I went in a corner and began rubbing my hands against my shoulders. I looked up in the sky and said, 'Jesus, if You be real, send someone by to pick me up.' And here you are."

Oh, this is just great, I thought sarcastically. *We've just been called an answer to his prayer.* Now I felt as though it was our responsibility to help him, and I just didn't want to.

When we got home, Dad kept a close eye on Nat. Mom was busy putting the finishing touches on the delicious Easter meal that she'd prepared the night before. Meanwhile Dad sat in the living room and chatted with Nat. Soon we found ourselves seated at the beautifully decorated dinner table.

Nat seemed very eager to get started with the meal. He licked his lips and rubbed his hands together like a man who hadn't eaten in years. I figured that he probably hadn't eaten in recent days at least.

The instant we finished saying grace, the sound of a serving spoon clanking against the inside of the mashed potato dish filled the room. It was Nat digging in, and he enthusiastically filled his plate to overflowing. We watched as he ate and ate and ate and then got some more. As he wolfed down bite after bite, my entire family stopped eating and simply watched him in amazement.

At last Nat finished eating, and we gathered around

the piano for family worship. After we finished singing the last song, Dad planned to take Nat back to the place where we had picked him up.

The last word was sung and the last chord on the piano was still ringing when Nat uttered the question that changed our lives for good. "Can I spend the night?"

At the time this question seemed completely outrageous to everyone in our family. Hadn't we done enough for him? My siblings and I were all in agreement, but Dad insisted that we hold a family meeting.

Mom tried to sway our opinions, telling us that this was a good man who needed our help. After she was through making her argument, my dad asked us all what we thought about the situation. My brother and I were beginning to soften, and we concluded it would be OK for just one night.

"You can stay the night, Nat," Dad said, "on one condition."

"What's that?"

"You have to take a bath."

"Sure," he said with a smile.

Soon we heard the sound of Nat taking a bath. Then, to our surprise, we heard the sound of the bathtub being drained and then refilled. It turned out that one bath wasn't enough. "After the first bath," Dad reported, "the bathtub sported a thick line of dirt and debris that encased the rim of the tub." My dad requested that Nat take another bath.

Nat didn't mind. "Hey, a great home-cooked meal and two baths in one day! I'd be honored to take another bath." So he did, and Nat probably came out cleaner than he'd been in several years.

Nat didn't stay for just one night. That night turned into weeks, and the weeks into months. Over that time my family gave him not just a cleaner body, but also a cleaner soul. He became a big part of our lives. We even started calling him Uncle Nat. We found his wife, and they got back together. He became a Christian and accepted Jesus as his Lord and Savior.

There was an old Bible in our house that Uncle Nat got very attached to and carried with him everywhere. Whenever we went to church he'd share with the members the story of how his life had been changed because we'd taken the risk of inviting him home. He would often say, "Guess who came to dinner and stayed!"

Looking back, I can see that God really did choose this man as an object of our compassion. God works everything out for the good of those who love Him. He used our family to change a man's life, and I'm so glad He did!

18

God's Smart Answer

by Jonelle Broady

Ben carefully arranged his report card on the table among the clutter of bills and junk mail. *Perhaps Mom won't notice it until after I go to bed*, he plotted.

He should have known better.

"Bennie, is this your report card?" Mom asked a short while later, ignoring the envelopes and zeroing right in on the folded manila card.

"Uh, yeah," Ben answered, pretending to be unconcerned.

Mom already knew that Ben wasn't doing well in math, but she had no idea that he was failing every other subject as well.

But Ben's classmates certainly knew. Everyone considered him to be the stupidest fifth grader at Higgins Elementary School.

Even worse, Ben believed them.

One time the class had actually debated over who was the class dummy. The other students had agreed that it was Ben. Ben was hurt, but he had finally agreed too.

"Benjamin Carson," Mom asked again, waving the card. "Are these your grades?"

"Yes, but they don't mean much."

"That's not true," Mom countered. "Education will be your escape from poverty."

Ben only half listened. Mom had often spoken of how she wanted Ben and his older brother, Curtis, to be more than factory floor sweepers.

"God expects more from you," she'd say.

Having made it through only third grade, Mom understood the importance of education—and the consequences of the lack of it. Since Ben's parents had separated, Mom was stuck cleaning houses to raise her sons.

"You're not living up to your potential. I know you can do better," she said.

"Yes, Mother," Ben replied dutifully, his chin drooping to meet his chest.

"You must work harder. Use the good brain that God gave you. Understand?" Mom asked.

"Yes, Mother."

"Rich folks do anything they want to do. So can you," Mom explained, lacing an arm around Ben's shoulder. "Except you can do it better."

Yeah, right, Ben thought, recalling again the day of the "dummy debate" at school. There had been a math quiz later that afternoon. After passing his paper to another student to be corrected and receiving it back, Ben discovered that his answers had earned him another fat zero.

The teacher was calling on everyone to report their scores aloud. Ben didn't want the kids to know that he'd gotten a zero. It would only reaffirm his "class dummy" status. But what could he do? He squirmed and clenched his lip between his teeth.

"Benjamin," Ms. Williamson called.

"Nnnne," Ben muttered anxiously, hoping she would misinterpret his words.

It worked.

"Nine! Benjamin, you got nine right?" Ms. Williamson exclaimed happily. "Good for you, Benjamin. I knew you could do it! Guess who's been studying, class."

The compliments went on and on.

Finally the girl who had corrected Ben's paper stood and announced, "He said, 'None'!"

The class exploded in laughter. Ms. Williamson sat down, embarrassed, and Ben pretended not to care.

The memory still hurt. *Now, does that sound like someone loaded with potential?* Ben wondered miserably.

"I know what to do," Mom was saying. "I'm going to talk to God about you and Curtis. The Lord will guide me, and we won't have any more poor report cards."

As Mom left, Ben sighed with relief, happy to end the report card ordeal. It could have been a lot worse.

The next two days passed like all the rest. Ben flunked another math test and performed just as wretchedly in spelling. But Ben's school woes would be forgotten by the time he and Curtis arrived home. There they dumped their books and scampered outside to join their friends in a game of softball or tip-the-top. Afterward, since Mom usually worked late, Ben and Curtis would spend the rest of the evening glued to the TV.

But that day Mom had something different in mind. She arrived home an hour early, strode across the room, and promptly turned off the television.

"Boys, you spend too much time in front of the TV," Mom began, crossing her arms over her chest. "I prayed for guidance, and the Lord told me what to do. You won't get an education this way. So from now on you will watch only two programs per week."

"Two shows? Out of a whole week?" Ben interrupted.

"And that's only after your homework is done. No going outside until your homework is done either."

Trying to defend their universe, Ben and Curtis spewed one objection after the next.

"I prayed for wisdom, and this is the answer I got," Mom repeated. "Also, along with your homework, you will read two books every week and prepare book reports for each one."

Mother paused to allow her words to sink in. "Do you both understand?"

The boys nodded, but Ben really didn't understand

at all. Just what kind of mother had he been stuck with?

After school the next day Curtis and Ben dragged themselves to the library. Since he liked animals, Ben chose the book *Chip, the Dam Builder,* about beavers. He surprised himself by reading it all the way through. He was even more stunned to discover he had enjoyed it.

On subsequent library visits Ben picked stories about squirrels, wolves, kangaroos, and snakes. When the animal books ran out, he read about plants, then minerals, then rocks. Ben learned to identify various stones at the railroad tracks near his home. He found that he could even follow along when Ms. Williamson asked someone to spell "agriculture."

Ben's life changed forever the day Mr. Jaeck, the science teacher, held up a black glasslike rock. Ben recognized it immediately.

"Can anyone identify this?" Mr. Jaeck asked.

No one answered—not even the smart kids.

Ben timidly raised his hand, aware of his classmates' snickering.

"Yes, Benjamin," Mr. Jaeck said.

"That's obsidian," Ben answered.

Mr. Jaeck's eyebrows rose as he said, "That's correct."

Ben continued, "It's formed when lava supercools as it hits water."

As jaws dropped all around him, Ben recited everything he remembered about the subject. When he finally finished, Mr. Jaeck's praise and the warm sensation of accomplishment Ben experienced made him feel as though he'd hit a jackpot!

Mom was right, Ben realized. *I do have a God-given brain, and I can use it. I don't have to be the dummy anymore!*

From then on Ben's love of reading grew. By the seventh grade he was at the top of his class. His mother's loving but tough decision had changed his life.

Ben added the Bible to his list of favorite books. He discovered that the words of wisdom and guidance written there could be used for any problem in his life.

Today Dr. Ben Carson still strives for excellence, and even though he is the director of the children's unit of neurosurgery at one of the top hospitals in the world, he has not lost his focus. Just as his mother taught him to do, Ben calls on God daily—for guidance of his hands during brain surgeries, for insight to help him make the right decisions for his patients, and sometimes even for miracles.

Ben is a Seventh-day Adventist, and his faith in God continues to grow. He is so thankful that his mother taught him to rely on God, and he says, "Never underestimate what God can do. Our best—no matter how good—is incomplete if we leave God out of the picture."

19

Ms. Maturity Has Arrived

by Melanie Scherencel Bockmann

I met Kelli Jo the summer after I turned 12. Kelli Jo was a year older than I was and had already started shaving her legs. This achievement earned her quite a bit of respect from the other girls (including me), who were not yet permitted such mature privileges.

Not only did she have experience with advanced hygiene practices, but Kelli Jo also knew a lot about boys. So when she decided to take me under her wing as her new best friend, I was honored.

"Boys like mature girls," Kelli Jo told me during one of her instructional sessions as we sat looking at magazines. "They can't stand girls who giggle all the time."

"Oh, of course—mature girls," I agreed, mentally vowing to never, ever giggle again.

"And don't ever cut your hair," Kelli Jo went on. "Boys like long hair—the longer, the better. That's why

I'm growing my hair out again." She stopped for a minute to examine her ponytail, and then she continued. "Boys like girls who are smart, but not too smart, so you should never get better grades than the guy you have a crush on."

"OK," I said, wondering if I should pull out a notebook and take notes. I was amazed by Kelli Jo's endless knowledge, and I knew that under her instruction, I could eventually be just as sophisticated as she was. She was truly the most mature girl I knew.

That night I was brushing my hair when my mom came into my room.

"You're brushing your hair before you go to bed?" Mom looked at me as if my neck had suddenly sprouted an extra head.

"Kelli Jo says that if I brush my hair 99 times every night before I go to bed, my hair will grow faster," I informed her.

Mom sat down on my flowered bedspread and smiled. "I've heard the words 'Kelli Jo says' quite a bit lately. I guess she's really been passing out a lot of advice."

"Well, she knows a lot," I responded.

Mom was quiet for a moment; then she said, "You know, Kelli Jo might know a lot of stuff, but there's an important element that she's missing. There's a difference between knowing things and being mature. Maturity comes from understanding who you are and what you're about, and Kelli Jo doesn't seem to have a lot of that."

"Mom," I said carefully, "don't take this wrong, but

it's been a long time since you were a teenager. Kelli Jo is, like, in touch."

I saw my mom's eyebrows go up, and at first I thought I was going to get a tongue-lashing. Instead she shook her head and gave me a hug. "One of these days," she said with a half-smile as she stood up, "you'll understand what your old, out-of-touch mother is talking about."

The next afternoon Kelli Jo made an announcement while she applied a fresh coat of lip gloss. "I think you're ready," she said, pressing her lips together and turning away from the mirror to face me.

"Ready?" I asked.

"Yeah, ready. I'm going to introduce you to some of my older friends," Kelli Jo answered with a flip of her ponytail. "You know, the mature ones I've been telling you about? I told them we'd meet them at the park in a few minutes."

I had no idea that my unofficial training had progressed to such an important milestone, and I tried not to show my nervousness. "Cool," I murmured.

When we arrived at the park, two older boys were waiting by the swings.

"Boys?" I looked at Kelli Jo in surprise. "I didn't know we were meeting boys."

Kelli Jo leaned toward me as we walked. "I told them you were mature. Don't let me down," she whispered.

"Hey," the taller, dark-haired boy said as we approached. He gave Kelli Jo a big hug.

"Hi, Paul," Kelli Jo said, smiling. She looked at the other boy and motioned to me. "Jake, this is the friend that I told you about."

I tried to smile, but my stomach started tying itself in knots. I could smell Jake's cologne; he was wearing so much of it that I was afraid the squirrels were going to faint and start dropping out of the trees.

"Hi," Jake said, looking into my eyes.

"Um, hi," I said back. The way he looked at me made me wish I had stayed at home.

Jake put his arm around me. "So, where do you want to go?" he asked.

"What are you doing?" I asked, pushing his arm off my shoulders.

Jake looked surprised, and then he smiled. He reached over and put his fingers in my hair. "You have great-looking hair," he said.

"Stop touching me," I demanded, pushing him away.

Jake seemed to lose his patience. He looked at Kelli Jo, who was hugging Paul. "I thought you said she was cool."

"I thought she was," Kelli Jo said, giving me a look that said "Shape up or else."

Paul jumped into the exchange. "Maybe you shouldn't have brought her."

"Yeah," Jake agreed. "Maybe she should go home and play with her dolls or something."

I waited for Kelli Jo to stick up for me. But she didn't.

"I'm sorry, guys," Kelli Jo said to the boys. Then she looked at me in apparent disgust. "I guess you're too young for this. Maybe you should just go."

My face felt hot. I looked at Kelli Jo for a moment and then turned to leave. Tears burned in my eyes, and I could hear their voices taunting me as I started walking as fast as I could away from the park.

So that was my big test of maturity? I thought as I kicked stones out of my path on my way home. *To let Jake run his sticky fingers through my hair and touch me like he owned me?* I knew that wasn't right. If Kelli Jo was wrong about that, what other stuff was she wrong about?

When I got home, I mentally gathered together all of Kelli Jo's so-called advice and trashed it, along with actually tossing out the magazines she had given me.

The weird thing was, even though it still hurt, I was glad that I'd walked away. Apparently—as my mom said—maturity does come from understanding who you are and what you're about. And that was something I had started to learn for myself.

20

Public Nuisance Number One

by Sandra Allen

The police had two words to describe John Fowler: public nuisance.

John's favorite part of being a nuisance was the public part of it. True, shoplifting required a certain amount of sneakiness, but once John had shoplifted, he had the satisfaction of adding "shoplifter" to his list of "being bad" crimes. How fun is that?

You, no doubt, are thinking, *Was he crazy? Who wants to be known as a shoplifter? a school dropout? a troublemaker?*

Well, hopefully you haven't gone down the path of destruction that John chose. You have been listening to your mother. You are in school. You don't take things that don't belong to you. You may be a nuisance sometimes, but the police don't know about it. People like you. They want to share their locker with you.

Not so with Bad Boy John. John was trouble and proud

of it. Trouble like "annoying, bothersome, disquieting, and disturbing."

Disquieting was John's specialty, especially disquieting the town of Collegedale, Tennessee. On a good day he disquieted the entire town and Collegedale Academy, a Seventh-day Adventist high school. (John had been a student at the academy before he began his career as a public nuisance.) On a good day, and there were many of them, John gleefully disquieted the academy enough to make them call off classes for the day. How fun is that?

It was simple, really. John had learned how to turn his Harley-Davidson into a large stick of dynamite—or at least that's how it sounded. Take the mufflers off. Put on twin echo pipes. Cycle up to a certain speed. Retard the spark. Gear down. Kapow! Instant dynamite! The noise was deafening. How fun is that?

John buzzed through Collegedale as if it were his own personal speedway and Collegedale Academy was the victory lap. John would wreak havoc—which means "cause destruction, create chaos, and play mischief"—in the town and the academy, and then "check out" before Officer Williams could get to him. (In case you haven't been hangin' around with any of John's friends, "check out" means he "went away fast." He "got ghost.") How fun is that?

People flooded the phone lines with complaints about John. The prevailing sentiment was that Mr. Williams, the town's police officer, an upholder of the law, should do something.

Officer Williams sighed. The public opinion of John was right. The law was very clear. Legally speaking, John had been lumped with rodents and telemarketers.

John paid as much attention to Officer Williams as if the man were a yapping dog. Mr. Williams had tried get-tough lectures, I-believe-in-you-John-you're-better-than-this speeches, descriptive soliloquies about the reality of being arrested, you're-hurting-your-mother-and-you-know-it-and-she-works-two-jobs-to-keep-food-on-the-table monologues, cajoling, pleading, and trying to be John's friend. Nothing worked. John's attitude was a bored, disinterested "Whatever, Mr. Williams." Officer Williams went away. John planned his next escapade.

Things changed the day Officer Williams arrested John. To John, "arrested" had been a far-off yapping sound that Mr. Williams made. In John's mind it wasn't real, and it certainly had nothing to do with him. But alas, Mr. Williams took him into custody under the authority of the law.

John was aghast—not to mention scared stiff. How could he, John Fowler, the bad boy of Collegedale, be arrested? What had he done to deserve this? What did Mr. Williams have against him? He was just having fun.

Court was a nightmare. Not the kind of nightmare that you'll wake up from and be glad that it was all a bad dream, but the kind of nightmare that's a bad experience and real.

The assistant district attorney read a long list of complaints—speeding, reckless driving, having a loud muffler, shoplifting, and being a public nuisance. Witnesses testified. Yep, John was bad. Rodents and telemarketers could just get in line.

The judge looked sternly at John. "How do you plead?"

"Guilty." What else could he say?

"Your fine is $60 or 60 days on the road gang, John."

John looked around the courtroom at the people he had hurt. The "wrong crowd" he ran with had disappeared as soon as John was arrested.

"Your Honor, I don't have any money," John answered.

"The only thing I can do is find you guilty. Since you don't have any money, I sentence you to 60 days on the chain gang. You'll earn $1 a day. In 60 days you can pay your fine off." The judge raised his gavel to dismiss the case.

Officer Williams interrupted. "Just a minute, Your Honor."

The police officer whispered urgently to John. "John, do you have any money? Can you borrow it from anybody? You don't belong on a chain gang!"

John shook his head.

Then Officer Williams did a shocking thing. He reached in his pocket and pulled out the bills that would set John free. "I'll pay his fine," he said.

Talk about a commotion! The judge, the witnesses, and John himself were astounded, astonished, jarred, and jolted. And as if those weren't enough synonyms for "shocked," they added on "offended, outraged, and appalled."

"I think you're crazy," said the judge. He was sure John had duped Officer Williams into believing in him. "Dupe" means "bamboozle," "befool," "flimflam," "hoodwink," and "hornswoggle."

But Mr. Williams hadn't been hornswoggled. Mr. Williams had a secret weapon. He saw John through God's eyes.

When the judge dismissed court, Officer Williams made his way over to John.

"I don't deserve this, Mr. Williams. You shouldn't have done it," John stammered.

Mr. Williams said, "Anything I can do to help you, let me know." Mr. Williams hugged John and walked away.

And that's the day John learned two other words: "mercy" and "grace." How fun is that?

By the way, John went on to become a pastor and eventually the president of a whole Seventh-day Adventist conference!

21

Heaping Coals on Kelsey Payne

by Christina Dotson

"I have had it with that girl!" I fumed as I stormed into the cabin and threw my towel onto the bed. "If she makes one more snobby comment, I'm going to wipe that smirk right off her face!"

My best friend, Mindy, leaned down from the top bunk. "Let me guess," she said. "Kelsey Payne strikes again."

"No kidding!" I exclaimed. "You know, that girl's last name really fits her. She's the biggest pain I've ever met."

I was so furious I thought I might explode. In the four years since I had been coming here to summer camp, I had never had to share a cabin with anyone like Kelsey Payne. Kelsey made friends by turning other people into enemies . . . and I was one of her enemies.

"So what did she do now?" Mindy asked.

"You'll never believe it," I said. "She offered to let me use her hairbrush!"

"Oh, no!" Mindy yelped. "Did you call the police?"

I glared. I was not in the mood for Mindy's jokes. "Very funny," I said. "But you know what Kelsey's like. There were a whole bunch of other girls in the bathroom, and Kelsey handed me her hairbrush because she said I looked like I really needed one. She even offered to teach me how to use it!"

My hands clenched just thinking about it. Kelsey loved to make fun of my flyaway, curly brown hair, which I was already sensitive about. I tried not to let her bother me, but there was something about that girl that just made me want to scream.

I was hoping Mindy could help me think of a way to get back at Kelsey, but before we could come up with anything we heard the whistle blow for breakfast. Revenge would have to wait.

I was still seething as I carried my tray through the breakfast line. In fact, I was so busy thinking about Kelsey that I wasn't paying attention to what I was doing. As I lifted a glass of orange juice from the counter, it slipped through my fingers and clattered loudly to the floor. Juice splashed all over, and for a brief moment the entire lodge was silent as everyone turned to stare.

"Nice one," said a voice from behind. "Real smooth."

I turned to face Kelsey Payne.

"I don't blame you for being clumsy," she said. "It must be hard to see with that frizzy mop hanging in your face. Maybe if you fixed your hair every once in a while . . ."

"At least I'm not obsessed with my hair like you!" I snapped. "You use so much hair spray it fogs up the entire bathroom. I'm surprised the Environmental Protection Agency hasn't come to arrest you yet. You're probably the leading cause of the hole in the ozone layer."

I was feeling pretty proud of my snappy comeback when I felt a hand on my shoulder. It was Sarah, our camp counselor. "Come on, girls," she said. "You're holding up the line. The custodian will mop up the juice."

Kelsey cast me one last smirk before flouncing off to our table. I was about to follow when Sarah pulled me aside. "Chris, I want to talk to you for a second," she said.

"I didn't do anything!" I exclaimed. "Kelsey's the one who—"

"You're not in trouble," said Sarah. "I just want to talk."

Reluctantly I followed her outside.

"I've noticed you and Kelsey really going at it," Sarah began. "You two have quite a feud going on."

"She started it," I protested. "I can't just sit and do nothing. She'll walk all over me!"

"I didn't say you should do nothing," Sarah replied. "But maybe you need to rethink how you're handling this."

"What do you mean?"

"What I mean is that Kelsey doesn't come from a Christian home. You do. Why don't you show her how Christians deal with their enemies?"

I sighed. "I'm guessing that doesn't involve dyeing her hair purple while she sleeps."

Sarah smiled. "I was thinking more along the lines of dumping coals of fire on her head. You know that Bible verse, right? Romans 12:20."

I sighed. I knew the verse, all right. I recited it half-heartedly. "'If your enemy is hungry, feed him; if he is thirsty, give him something to drink. In doing this, you will heap burning coals on his head' [NIV]."

"Exactly," said Sarah. "The Bible tells us that if we're kind to our enemies, they just might become our friends." She patted my shoulder as she headed back inside. "Think about it."

So I did. I thought about it all morning long. *Maybe I should make the first move toward being nice to Kelsey—but how?* I wondered.

That afternoon, when it was our cabin's turn to visit the pool, I saw my chance to drop a coal of kindness on Kelsey Payne's head.

The most popular pool activity was to paddle around on the small foam kickboards provided by the pool staff. The campers had invented all kinds of games that could be played only while balancing on a kickboard, yet there were never enough boards to go around.

I had gotten to the pool early and already had a board, but I noticed that Kelsey did not. She sat at the edge of the water, dangling her feet in and watching her friends organize a kickboard race. Gathering my nerve and swallowing my pride, I swam up beside her. "Do you want my kickboard?" I asked, holding it out. "I'm not going to use it anymore."

Kelsey recoiled as if I were handing her a live barracuda. "What would I want that for?" she sneered.

I shrugged and set the board down beside her. "It's yours if you change your mind," I said.

I thought that would be the end of it. I forgot that Kelsey always liked to have the last word. As I paddled away, she shouted loudly after me, "It's not going to work, you know! Did you really think giving me your dumb kickboard was going to make me be your friend? You're more pathetic than I thought!"

I felt my face grow warm with embarrassment as several nearby campers turned to watch us curiously. I longed to whirl around and face Kelsey, dunk her underwater, yell and scream, and let the whole camp know that I wouldn't be her friend if she paid me.

What was I thinking, anyway? I couldn't be nice to this girl. She was impossible! The best I could manage at the moment was to ignore her and swim away. I headed for the deep end of the pool and began swimming laps to calm myself down.

As I paused to catch my breath, I caught sight of Kelsey at the other end of the pool. I watched as she glanced around, made sure no one was looking, then casually picked up the kickboard, jumped into the water, and paddled over to her friends.

That should have made me feel better . . . but it didn't. Nothing had changed between Kelsey and me, and I doubted that even 1,000 good deeds would make a difference. Maybe I just wasn't cut out for this whole "loving your enemy" thing.

A few days later as the camp bus pulled up alongside the river, my spirits rose for the first time in days. Of all the camp activities, canoeing was my favorite. I was determined to have a good time and to forget all about Kelsey Payne.

"Come on, Mindy!" I said, grabbing my friend by the arm. "Let's go pick out our canoe."

I waited impatiently near the water's edge while the instructors reminded us of the rules. As I glanced around at the rest of the group, I spotted Kelsey standing by herself, holding a life jacket at arm's length as if it had fleas. Everyone else was grouped near whomever they planned to canoe with, but Kelsey stood alone.

I looked around for Kelsey's friends, the small group of girls she was always giggling with in the bathroom, the ones she liked to show off for by poking fun at me. Finally I spotted them. They had already claimed a canoe for themselves, and there was obviously no room for Kelsey.

Mindy, seeming to read my mind, leaned over and whispered, "I heard them say they're sick of Kelsey. They say she's too stuck-up. Serves her right, huh?"

"Yeah . . . I guess," I replied.

I tried not to think about Kelsey. I didn't want to

feel sorry for her. I had given up on trying to be her friend. Even so, the words of Romans 12:20 kept running through my head: "If your enemy is hungry, feed him; if he is thirsty, give him something to drink. In doing this, you will heap burning coals on his head."

"You're going to invite her to share our canoe, aren't you?" said Mindy.

"Do you mind?" I asked.

Mindy shrugged. "If you can handle it, I can."

I wasn't expecting Kelsey to say yes. In fact, I was really hoping she wouldn't. That way I could feel good about being nice without having to actually put up with her.

I was very surprised when she accepted my invitation.

"Fine, I'll ride with you," Kelsey said, as if she were doing me a favor. "But I'm not sitting in the middle. There's no seat in the middle, and my pants will get wet."

"OK," I said through clenched teeth.

"And I'm not sitting behind you, either," she added as she flounced off toward the riverbank. "That bunch of weeds you call hair is liable to fly back and take my eye out."

I swallowed an angry response as I let Kelsey take the front of the canoe. I helped Mindy push the boat into the water, and we headed off down the river.

All around us the other campers were yelling and splashing excitedly, but our canoe was silent. I was having trouble paddling from my spot in the middle of the canoe, yet I had to try because Kelsey refused even to place her paddle in the water.

I was sorely tempted to rock the canoe until we capsized. Mindy wouldn't mind if it meant we could soak Kelsey's perfectly sculpted hairdo. I had to keep reminding myself that the only real way to destroy an enemy was to turn that enemy into a friend.

We continued slowly down the river. One by one the other canoes began passing us by. Soon the boat carrying Kelsey's former friends pulled ahead of us. I saw Kelsey's shoulders stiffen. She stared straight ahead.

The girls in the other canoe waved. "Hi, Mindy! Hi, Chris!" they called out. They were obviously making sure Kelsey knew she was being ignored.

As the girls' canoe rounded the bend and disappeared from sight, I heard Kelsey sniffle and saw her wipe her face with the back of her hand.

Is she crying? I wondered. *Should I say something?*

Before I had a chance to decide, another canoe pulled up and nearly bumped us from behind. "Beep, beep! Move over, slowpokes!" The three boys in the canoe splashed us playfully as they zipped by. "It might be faster if you got out and walked," they laughed.

That was the last straw. Not for me, but for Kelsey. Without warning she leaped to her feet, waving her paddle in the air and shouting, "Come back and say that to my face!"

Whoa! Mindy and I exchanged surprised glances

as we tried to steady the canoe. Had Kelsey completely snapped?

"You'd better sit down," said Mindy. "We're going to tip over."

Kelsey sat, but she was still fuming. "Those . . . those guys," she sputtered.

"You know," I said hesitantly, not sure how Kelsey would react, "we could race them. If we won, that would teach them to call us slow."

Kelsey turned to look me in the face. I imagined she was thinking the same thing I was. Racing would mean we'd have to work together. Could we do it? Did we want to do it?

It was Kelsey who made the final decision. "OK," she said. "Let's race!"

Immediately the three of us began paddling with all our hearts.

"We're coming!" Mindy called out to the boys ahead.

"Go, go, go!" I whooped.

"Paddle! Paddle!" Kelsey yelled.

United by a common goal, we started working together. Kelsey watched for debris in the water and warned us before we hit anything. Mindy provided the steering, and I taught Kelsey how to determine which side of the canoe to paddle on. We were turning into a regular team when trouble struck.

None of us saw the underwater log until we crashed into it. The next thing we knew, the current had carried our boat sideways, pressing us against the log. We were stuck.

I watched miserably as the boys' canoe pulled even farther ahead. I couldn't let this happen! We were getting along so well! I wasn't going to give up now!

Without thinking I leaped over the side of the canoe. The sudden rush of cold water up to my shoulders took my breath away. The current was much stronger than I'd expected. I tried pushing the canoe free, but it was no use. I couldn't do it.

Suddenly I heard a loud splash, and Kelsey Payne was by my side. I could hardly believe my eyes. My mouth dropped open, and I choked on river water.

"Come on!" Kelsey urged. "You push and I'll pull."

"And I'll stay here where it's warm and dry," Mindy added.

Working together, Kelsey and I managed to free the canoe. We pushed for a while to get it going before slipping and sliding in our struggle to climb back in.

"You guys look like swamp rats," Mindy laughed as we lay gasping in the boat. "I'm going to tell everyone I tied bricks to your shoes and dragged you along the bottom."

Kelsey and I looked at each other. Sure enough, we were covered from head to toe with muddy water. There was even mud on our faces, and our hair was soaked. We began laughing so hard we could barely hold our paddles.

"So much for not getting my clothes wet, huh?" Kelsey gasped.

"Hey, look!" I exclaimed. "My hair isn't frizzy anymore!"

The smile vanished from Kelsey's face. There was a moment of uncomfortable silence as we both remembered that we were supposed to be enemies.

"Yeah . . ." said Kelsey. "About that . . ."

"Hey, look!" Mindy exclaimed, pointing downstream. "The boys ran their canoe into a rock! We can still beat them!"

"Let's go!" I yelled.

Kelsey cast me a grateful look before dipping her paddle into the water. I replied with a smile. Somehow we both knew that the other was sorry and that things would be different from now on. And anyway, words aren't always necessary between friends.

22

Stones From Heaven

as told to Brenda Segna by Luise Werner

"Lord, please help us to build a church," Nabirye prayed as the rain ran along the ends of her raven-black hair and onto her neck. She shook her head to make the drops fly. Nabirye and her family had been praying for a church for as long as the young girl could remember. Nabirye lived in Africa, where there was more prayer than money when it came to building a church.

In the middle of Africa is a mountain range called the Rwenzori Mountains, or the Mountains of the Moon. East of the mountains is Uganda, and on the western side the Congo stretches out as far as the eye can see.

At the foot of the mountains on the Congolese side was a group of Adventists with about 50 members. They were mostly women who worshipped God every Sabbath in a church made of sticks with mud smeared between them, topped with a grass-thatched roof.

Next to the church was a river, with a road that led from the Congo to Uganda. On the other side of the road was a very big and beautiful church where the members worshipped God on Sundays.

Nabirye and all the members of the Adventist church dreamed about having their own big church just like the one on the other side of the road.

"If only we had a nicer church," Nabirye said, looking at her stick church. "If only . . ."

"Let's pray," said Nabirye's mother, and that's just what they did. "Dear Lord, please give us stones so that we can build a church."

Twelve-year-old Seif, who attended the other church, heard about the prayers of Nabirye and the Sabbathkeepers. "You think God will rain stones from heaven?" he asked Nabirye mockingly.

The youngsters stood by the river that ran near the church. "God will hear our prayers, and yes, I believe He will send stones," Nabirye insisted.

Many of the people from the other church started mocking the Sabbathkeepers. But Nabirye and the Adventist church members didn't care, because they knew that God would hear their prayers and answer according to His will.

A few days later there was a terrible storm in the Rwenzori Mountains. It was so severe that many stones were loosened. They came tumbling down the mountains and were carried downstream by the river. The flooded river piled all of those stones on the land next to the Adventists' mud-and-thatch church.

The church members thanked the Lord and started carrying all the stones to the place where they wanted the church built.

Now the church members needed a builder. "Dear Lord," they prayed, "please send someone to build our church."

They prayed. They waited. They prayed some more. And just a day's journey by car from the small group of praying church members was the Adventist mission station of Rwese. Near the station lived an African Adventist named Petro, who was very wealthy—and a builder as well.

Petro was a very gifted man who had built many beautiful government buildings. He heard about the church group near the Rwenzori Mountains and their prayer for a builder.

Petro wondered about the stones. He wondered about the church they prayed for. And he knew that God wanted him to visit the Adventist group. So he went to meet these believers.

Nabirye showed him the pile of stones. She would have asked question after question, but the man was looking down at the pile of rocks, praying.

They stood there for a long time. Nabirye's toes were numb, and so were her ankles. Petro stood stone-still, almost as if he were part of the rocks. He was satisfied.

"I will build a church large enough for 100 members," he told Nabirye and the other church members.

"Oh, no," said Nabirye's mother. "We want a church for 500 people."

"But you have only a few members," replied Petro, shaking his head. What was the point in building a larger church than necessary?

"The God who rained stones from heaven can also fill a church with room for 500 people," Nabirye said. "We must believe."

"I believe God sent you stones, so it should be no problem for Him to send you church members, too," Petro said. So he and his helpers built a very big and beautiful church that would hold 500 members.

When the church was finished, the Adventists asked a pastor to come and dedicate their church.

Seif and the members from his church had watched all these miracles as they happened.

"I'm sorry," Seif said to Nabirye—and he truly was. "God really did answer your prayers. I shouldn't have made fun of you."

"I forgive you," Nabirye said. "Would you like to come to the dedication service for our new church?"

"Really?" Seif said with a smile the size of a cantaloupe slice. Not only did Seif go to the Adventist church for the dedication, but all the people from the church across the road attended. They filled the church. And they came the next week and the next. Eventually they were baptized and became members of the Seventh-day Adventist Church. God had filled the church, just as Nabirye believed. Nabirye and all the church members learned that God hears and answers prayers.

23

Rafael's Choice

by Patti Emanuele

The front of the T-shirt held an image of a dying gang member. It announced that Rafael belonged to a specific gang.

"Never take this off," the gang leader had warned him. Rafael had obeyed. Complete loyalty to the gang was expected.

Rafael didn't really like belonging to a gang. What he really thrived on was painting and drawing.

"Why did God make me this way?" Rafael wondered out loud. He hid his talents from the members of his gang. If they found out, there would be real trouble. He was supposed to care only about gang business.

Rafael wanted to shout that he didn't even want to be a gang member. Sometimes he wanted to be free like his friend Alex from school. But in Rafael's world there seemed to be no way out of his lifestyle.

One day Macy, a small boy in Rafael's neighborhood, said to him, "Someday I wanna be in a gang like you. I can't wait until I'm old enough to get my own T-shirt."

Rafael shuddered. This boy was watching him. Rafael felt as if he were leading this little boy into a life of crime. He glanced down at his T-shirt and resisted the temptation to rip it off.

"You could be an example to Macy," Alex told Rafael one day after school. "If you turned your life over to Jesus, you could teach him that Jesus, not the gang, will fill his life." The two boys walked toward Alex's apartment complex. Rafael glanced upward toward Alex's apartment. He saw the curtains move. Rafael knew it was Alex's mother watching for her son to come home. Rafael felt a pang in his heart. Rafael's home was so different.

"It's OK to be who God made you," his friend Alex continued. "Look at me—I can paint, draw pictures, take photos, and still be cool." Alex gave Rafael a friendly punch on the arm. "When you turn your life over to Jesus, He uses your gifts to give you the best life you can have."

Rafael shook his head. "You don't get it, man. You've never belonged to a gang."

The two boys had both grown up in the projects. Yet somehow Alex had escaped gang life. He had poured his energy into his church. His mother had propelled him there, insisting that every free moment be spent in service to others and that his loyalty to Jesus be unquestioned. Rafael envied Alex and his life, yet he was afraid of quitting the gang.

"Jesus is there for you, man," Alex reminded Rafael. "I could ask my youth leader to visit you. Better yet, come to church with me this weekend," Alex encouraged.

Rafael thought about his friend's invitation. He knew that his allegiance was supposed to be to the gang—not to art, not to Jesus. But he also knew that if he continued his life with the gang, his future would be jail or something worse.

"I want out of this," Rafael told another friend, Manuel, after school one day. The two boys were headed for their hangout, an empty basement of a "blown-out" warehouse. There were many buildings like that one in the city, marked by scars left from gang wars and vandalism.

Manuel was silent. When they reached the warehouse, he found a used cigarette on the cement floor and lit it with his last match. He inhaled slowly and breathed out a stream of smoke. Manuel had smoked cigarettes—and worse—for several years. He was 12 years old.

"Alex told me that I can have a different life if I follow Jesus," Rafael told Manuel.

"Church talk," Manuel muttered.

Just then the door burst open. "Get outta here!" Ralph, a fellow gang member, shouted. "They're comin' here for you," he said, pointing to Rafael. "There's gonna be trouble."

"Wh-what?" Rafael stammered.

"Tommy heard that you draw pictures. He said they're gonna teach you how you should be spendin' your time."

Rafael glanced over at Manuel. "How did they find out?" he asked.

Manuel shifted uneasily. "Look, you gotta learn. It's for your own good." He turned away from Rafael.

So that was it. Manuel had ratted on him. Rafael pushed past Manuel and bolted out the door.

"There's no place to hide," Manuel shouted after Rafael.

As he ran down the street Rafael spotted the church that Alex attended. He darted inside.

It was quiet and dark in the sanctuary. Rafael felt a sense of peace come over him.

"Something I can do for you?" a young man wearing a "Jesus Lives" T-shirt asked.

Rafael was suddenly aware of the dying gang member printed across his own shirt. The man glanced at it and then gazed steadily into Rafael's eyes.

"Something wrong?" the man probed gently.

"I need help," Rafael blurted out.

"My name is John. I'm the youth pastor here. Come with me, and we'll figure this out together," the man told Rafael as he led him to his downstairs office.

As Rafael gazed around the small office, his eyes settled on an open Bible on the youth pastor's desk.

After Rafael explained his problem, John cleared his throat and said, "You need to understand, you're not alone. Jesus is here with you."

Just then Rafael heard a commotion in the sanctuary. His gang had entered the church. "We'll find him," Rafael heard Tommy tell his gang.

"We need to pray," the pastor told Rafael.

Rafael bowed his head, with a deliberate effort to block out the noise outside the room, and asked Jesus into his life.

Rafael and John walked upstairs. They spotted Tommy, who smiled slowly and wickedly. Behind him the other gang members lined up, awaiting instructions.

Vivid images of past street fights popped into Rafael's head. He knew what kind of "lesson" the gang could teach him.

Rafael thought about his bedroom with its walls covered in paintings and a half-finished canvas propped up on his table. Rafael loved the way the colors came alive and his imagination erupted onto the blank canvas. Creating something unique made him feel free from the poverty that he knew all too well. Alex was right—God had made Rafael unique.

Rafael knew it was time for a decision: Would he grow up and be a gang member or choose to follow God and use the gifts He'd given Rafael as an artist?

Thank You for making me just as I am, Rafael prayed silently. *Protect us, Lord.*

Pastor John and Rafael faced the gang together. With determination Rafael pulled the T-shirt from his body.

"I don't belong to the gang anymore," he said boldly. "I belong to Jesus."

The boys stared at Rafael. Minutes passed, feeling like hours.

Tommy cleared his throat.

This is it, Rafael told himself. He clenched his fist.

"It takes guts to quit," Tommy said to Rafael. "This Jesus must be strong." Slowly Tommy and his gang shuffled out of the church.

When young Macy heard that Rafael had quit the gang, he asked him, "Whose gang are you in now?"

Rafael put his arm around Macy's shoulders and said, "Let me tell you about Jesus."

24

Desperate for Air

by Wayne Carey

I don't remember who started talking about diving off the bridge across the river, but it seemed exciting to me! "It really isn't that high. I can do it," I bragged to my friends.

The bridge had three concrete buttresses for support. The middle one was round and stood in the center of the river. As we reached the center of the bridge I gave a few more bragging words and slowly slipped through the small opening that led to the ledge on the buttress.

The ledge was about two feet wide and seven feet up from the water. A narrow sandbar had formed directly below it from the water flowing around the buttress. I knew the sandbar was there, so I moved to the far edge, where the water would be deeper.

I looked at the water flowing below me as the gentle current pushed it toward the bay. The bridge seemed higher than I had thought. Now I wished I had never bragged that I would dive off. I was actually afraid!

My friends watched from above. I knew they were thinking I was scared. I had to dive just to prove I wasn't.

Why did I ever get myself into such a predicament? I thought. My mother had warned me to stay away from the bridge because it was dangerous. But mothers always seem to worry a lot.

The day had been perfect up until that moment. Yet God had never crossed my mind all afternoon. I figured I would have plenty of time to think about God when I grew older, because right then I was having too much fun spending time with my friends.

I stood there taking deep breaths to stall for more time and to get as much oxygen into my lungs as possible. How I wished no one was there! *If my friends weren't watching, I could just go back home*, I thought.

I stood on the ledge a moment longer, taking several more deep breaths and staring at the water. Crouching a little, I took one more gulp of air and then dove headfirst into the river below.

I found myself at the bottom of the river. It was so quiet—so awfully quiet—and the water was so cold. I tried to swim to the surface, but I couldn't move. My body was limp. *Oh, God!* my heart cried out. *Help me!*

I couldn't swim to the surface, to fresh air, to life. *What have I done?* I thought. *I'll drown for sure unless—unless what?* I didn't know.

Earlier I had not thought about God, but now without His help I would die! I was only 14 years old, and I wasn't prepared to die. *Is this really happening to me? Oh, God, please!*

I could feel myself slowly floating upward. I had to keep holding my breath—but how long could I do that? Each second seemed like an hour.

The water grew warmer. *I must be nearer the surface. Someone help me! I don't want to die. Please! If only I could breathe!*

My lungs felt like they would burst any second. Somehow I kept holding my breath.

I felt my back bob to the surface, but my face was still underwater. I was so close to life—just inches away—but I couldn't move. I tried and tried to get my head up out of the water. I couldn't. *There's no hope*, I thought.

Then I heard muffled sounds, but I couldn't tell what they were. Suddenly I felt the water around me moving. A hand grabbed me and pulled my head up. I remember the bright sun flooding my eyes . . . the rush of air into my lungs. *I can breathe! Oh, God, I can breathe!* It was the most wonderful thing in the world. I was alive!

One of my buddies had seen me floating in the water and had climbed down the buttress and pulled me to the sandbar. The fire department had been called, and when the firefighters arrived, they lowered a boat into the water to bring me to the riverbank. An ambulance came to take me to the hospital. I was so scared, but I was alive.

God had answered my simple prayer. I felt like Peter, who had cried out, "Lord, save me!" when he walked on the water and began to sink. His prayer was not fancy or eloquent, but it was very fervent. Jesus had saved Peter, and He had saved me from drowning.

It was several months before I left the hospital. I had struck something under the water that had cut open my scalp, so I received 21 stitches to my head. The impact had also crushed a vertebra in my neck, causing partial paralysis.

The heartbreak and agony of being paralyzed at 14 years old were almost unbearable. But because I was young, and with healing and therapy, most of the movement came back. I wore a neck brace for six months after leaving the hospital.

Many times in the years that followed I looked back to this experience and realized how precious life is and how quickly it can end. Sometime later I asked Jesus into my life. He saved me physically *and* spiritually! He has given my life meaning and purpose.

I ended up going into the ministry and being pastor of a church. I direct people who are drowning in sin to call on Jesus to save them. He gives life, and He is the bridge to heaven.